NEWNES
RADIO AND
ELECTRONICS
ENGINEER'S
POCKET BOOK

Revised by
the editorial Staff of
Electronics Today International

GW00361173

NEWNES–BUTTERWORTHS
LONDON · BOSTON
Sydney · Wellington · Durban · Toronto

THE BUTTERWORTH GROUP

UNITED KINGDOM
Butterworth & Co (Publishers) Ltd.
London: 88 Kingsway, WC2B 6AB

AUSTRALIA
Butterworths Pty Ltd
Sydney: 586 Pacific Highway, Chatswood, NSW 2067
Also at Melbourne, Brisbane, Adelaide and Perth

CANADA
Butterworth & Co. (Canada) Ltd
Toronto: 2265 Midland Avenue, Scarborough,
Ontario M1P 4S1

NEW ZEALAND
Butterworths of New Zealand Ltd
Wellington: T & W Young Building
77–85 Customhouse Quay, 1, CPO Box 472

SOUTH AFRICA
Butterworth & Co (South Africa) (Pty) Ltd
Durban: 152–154 Gale Street

USA
Butterworth (Publishers) Inc
Boston: 10 Tower Office Park, Woburn, Mass. 01801

First published 1940 by George Newnes Ltd
Thirteenth edition 1962
Fourteenth edition 1972 by Newnes–Butterworths
Fifteenth edition 1978, Reprinted 1979
© Butterworth & Co. (Publishers) Ltd, 1978

ISBN 0 408 00314 6

Printed in Great Britain by
Fletcher & Son Ltd, Norwich

PREFACE

Keeping reference books up to date is becoming an increasingly difficult task. This edition has major changes over those made in 1972.

The widespread use of the pocket calculator has enabled us to leave out much material which was very useful a few years ago but is now redundant. This has been done in order to make room for a mass of new information, much of which relates to integrated circuits.

Our criterion for choosing what to include has been 'What do *we* look up?' We have put in some information which is not available elsewhere, even though it may be needed only infrequently.

A reference book is only as good as its index and for this reason great care has been taken in its compilation.

H. W. Moorshead
R. Harris
J. Perry

Electronics Today International

CONTENTS

ABBREVIATIONS AND SYMBOLS

A	Ampere or anode
ABR	Auxiliary bass radiator
a.c.	Alternating current
A/D	Analogue to digital
Ae	Aerial
a.f.	Audio frequency
a.f.c.	Automatic frequency control
a.g.c.	Automatic gain control
a.m.	Amplitude modulation
ASA	Acoustical Society of America
ASCII	American Standard Code for Information Interchange
a.t.u.	Aerial tuning unit
AUX	Auxiliary
a.v.c.	Automatic volume control
b	Base of transistor
BAF	Bonded acetate fibre
B & S	Brown & Sharpe (U.S.) wire gauge
BR	Bass reflex
C	Capacitor, cathode, centigrade, charge or the speed of light
c	Collector of transistor
CB	Citizen's band
CCD	Charge coupled device
CCIR	International Radio Consultative Committee
CCTV	Closed circuit television
c.g.s.	Centimetre-gram-second system of units
chps	Characters per second
CPU	Central processor unit
CTD	Charge transfer device
CLK	Clock signal
CrO_2	Chromium dioxide
CMOS	Complementary metal oxide semiconductor
c.w.	Continuous wave
D	Diode
d	Drain of an f.e.t.
D/A	Digital to analogue
dB	Decibel
d.c.	Direct current
DCC	Double cotton covered
DF	Direction finding
DIL	Dual-in-line
DIN	German standards institute

9

DPDT	Double pole, double throw
DPST	Double pole, single throw
DSC	Double silk covered
DTL	Diode-transistor logic
DX	Long distance reception
e	Emitter of transistor
EAROM	Electrically alterable read only memory
ECL	Emitter coupled logic
e.h.t.	Extremely high tension (voltage)
e.m.f.	Electromotive force
en	Enamelled
EQ	Equalisation
ERP	Effective radiated power
EROM	Erasable read only memory
F	Farad, fahrenheit or force
f	Frequency
Fe	Ferrous
FeCr	Ferri-chrome
f.e.t.	Field effect transistor
f.m.	Frequency modulation
f.r.	Frequency response or range
f.s.d.	Full-scale deflection
G	Giga (10^9)
g	Grid, gravitational constant
H	Henry
h.f.	High frequency
Hz	Hertz (cycles per second)
I	Current
IB	Infinite baffle
i.c.	Integrated circuit
I.F.	Intermediate frequency
IHF	Institute of High Fidelity (U.S.)
I²L(IIL)	Integrated injection logic
i.m.d.	Intermodulation distortion
i/p	Input
i.p.s.	Inches per second
k	Kilo (10^3) or cathode
L	Inductance or lumens
l.e.d.	Light emitting diode
l.f.	Low frequency
LIN	Linear
LOG	Logarithmic
LS	Loudspeaker
LSI	Large scale integration

l.w.	Long wave (approx. 1100–2000 m)
M	Mega (10^6)
m	Milli (10^{-3}) or metres
MHz	Megahertz
mmF	Sometimes used for picofarad
m.c.	Moving coil
mic	Microphone
MOS	Metal oxide semiconductor
MPU	Microprocessor unit
MPX	Multiplex
m.w.	Medium wave (approx. 185–560 m)
n	Nano (10^{-9})
NAB	National Association of Broadcasters
Ni-Cad	Nickel-cadmium
n/c	Not connected; normally closed
n/o	Normally open
NMOS	Negative channel metal oxide semiconductor
o/c	Open channel; open circuit
OCL	Output capacitor-less
o/p	Output
op-amp	Operational amplifier
OTL	Output, transformerless
p	Pico (10^{-12})
PA	Public address
PAL	Phase alternation, line
p.a.m.	Pulse amplitude modulation
PCB	Printed circuit board
PLL	Phase locked loop
PMOS	Positive channel metal oxide semiconductor
P.P.M.	Peak programme meter
p.r.f.	Pulse repetition frequency
PROM	Programmable read only memory
PSU	Power supply unit
PTFE	Polytetrafluorethylene
PU	Pickup
PUJT	Programmable unijunction transistor
Q	Quality factor; efficiency of tuned circuit
R	Resistance
RAM	Random access memory
RCF	Recommended crossover frequency
RIAA	Record Industry Association of America
r.f.	Radio frequency
r.f.c.	Radio frequency choke (coil)
r.m.s.	Root mean square

RTL	Resistor transistor logic
R/W	Read/write
RX	Receiver
s/c	Short circuit
SCR	Silicon-controlled rectifier
s.h.f.	Super high frequency
S/N	Signal-to-noise
SPL	Sound pressure level
SPST	Single pole, single throw
SPDT	Single pole, double throw
SSI	Small scale integration
s.w.	Short wave (approx. 10–60 m)
s.w.g.	Standard wire gauge
s.w.r.	Standing wave ratio
t.h.d.	Total harmonic distortion
t.i.d.	Transient intermodulation distortion
TR	Transformer
t.r.f.	Tuned radio frequency
TTL	Transistor transistor logic
TTY	Teletype unit
TVI	Television interface; television interference
TX	Transmitter
u.h.f.	Ultra high frequency (approx. 470–854 MHz)
u.j.t.	Unijunction transistor
V	Volts
VA	Volt-amps
v.c.o.	Voltage controlled oscillator
VCT	Voltage to current transactor
v.h.f.	Very high frequency (approx. 88–216 MHz)
v.l.f.	Very low frequency
VU	Volume unit
W	Watts
W/F	Wow and flutter
w.p.m.	Words per minute
X	Reactance
Xtal	Crystal
Z	Impedance
ZD	Zener diode

GREEK ALPHABET

Capital letters	Small letters	Greek name	English equivalent
A	α	*Alpha*	a
B	β	*Beta*	b
Γ	γ	*Gamma*	g
Δ	δ	*Delta*	d
E	ε	*Epsilon*	e
Z	ζ	*Zeta*	z
H	η	*Eta*	é
Θ	θ	*Theta*	th
I	ι	*Iota*	i
K	κ	*Kappa*	k
Λ	λ	*Lambda*	l
M	μ	*Mu*	m
N	ν	*Nu*	n
Ξ	ξ	*Xi*	x
O	ο	*Omicron*	ŏ
Π	π	*Pi*	p
P	ρ	*Rho*	r
Σ	ς	*Sigma*	s
T	τ	*Tau*	t
Υ	υ	*Upsilon*	u
Φ	φ	*Phi*	ph
X	χ	*Chi*	ch
Ψ	ψ	*Psi*	ps
Ω	ω	*Omega*	ö

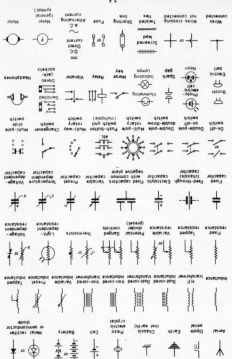

COMPONENT SYMBOLS

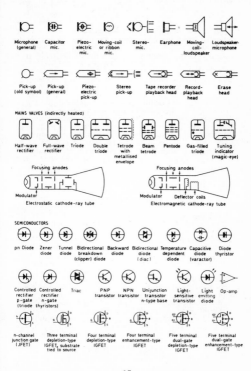

Microphone (general)   Capacitor mic.   Piezo-electric mic.   Moving-coil or ribbon mic.   Stereo-mic.   Earphone   Moving-coil-loudspeaker   Loudspeaker-microphone

Pick-up (old symbol)   Pick-up (general)   Piezo-electric pick-up   Stereo pick-up   Tape recorder playback head   Record-playback head   Erase head

MAINS VALVES (indirectly heated)

Half-wave rectifier   Full-wave rectifier   Triode   Double triode   Tetrode with metallised envelope   Beam tetrode   Pentode   Gas-filled triode   Tuning indicator (magic-eye)

Focusing anodes

Modulator

Electrostatic cathode-ray tube

Focusing anodes

Modulator   Deflector coils

Electromagnetic cathode-ray tube

SEMICONDUCTORS

pn Diode   Zener diode   Tunnel diode   Bidirectional breakdown (clipper) diode   Backward diode   Bidirectional diode (diac)   Temperature dependent diode   Capacitive diode (varactor)   Diode thyristor

Controlled rectifier p-gate   Controlled rectifier n-gate (triode thyristors)   Triac   PNP transistor   NPN transistor   Unijunction transistor n-type base   Light-sensitive transistor   Light emitting diode   Op-amp

n-channel junction gate (JFET)   Three terminal depletion-type IGFET, substrate tied to source   Four terminal depletion-type IGFET   Four terminal enhancement-type IGFET   Five terminal dual-gate depletion-type IGFET   Five terminal dual-gate enhancement-type IGFET

15

STANDARD UNITS

Ampere—Unit of electric current, the constant current which, if maintained in two straight parallel conductors of infinite length of negligible circular cross-section and placed one metre apart in a vacuum, will produce between them a force equal to 2×10^{-7} newton per metre length.

Ampere-hour—Unit of quantity of electricity equal to 3,600 coulombs. One unit is represented by one ampere flowing for one hour.

Coulomb—Unit of electric charge, the quantity of electricity transported in one second by one ampere.

Farad—Unit of electric capacitance. The capacitance of a capacitor between the plates of which there appears a difference of potential of one volt when it is charged by one coulomb of electricity. In radio, practical units are the microfarad (10^{-6} farad), the nanofarad (10^{-9}) and the picofarad (10^{-12} farad).

Henry—Unit of electrical inductance. The inductance of a closed circuit in which an electromotive force of one volt is produced when the electric current in the circuit varies uniformly at the rate of one ampere per second. In radio, practical units are the microhenry (10^{-6} henry) and the millihenry (10^{-3} henry).

Hertz—Unit of frequency. The number of repetitions of a regular occurrence in one second.

Joule—Unit of energy, including work and quantity of heat. The work done when the point of application of a force of one newton is displaced through a distance of one metre in the direction of the force.

Kilovolt-ampere—1,000 volt-amperes.

Kilowatt—1,000 watts.

Mho—Unit of conductance, see Siemens.

Newton—Unit of force. That force which, applied to a mass of one kilogram, gives it an acceleration of one metre per second per second.

Ohm—Unit of electric resistance. The resistance between two points of a conductor when a constant difference of potential of one volt, applied between these two points, produces in the conductor a current of one ampere.

Picofarad—10^{-12} farad.

Siemens—Unit of conductance, the reciprocal of the ohm. A body having a resistance of 4 ohms would have a conductance of 0·25 siemens.

Tesla—Unit of magnetic flux density, equal to one weber per square metre of circuit area.

Volt—Unit of electric potential. The difference of electric potential between two points of a conducting wire carrying a constant current of one ampere, when the power dissipated between these points is equal to one watt.

Volt-ampere—The product of the root-mean-square volts and root-mean-square amperes.

Watt—Unit of power, equal to one joule per second. Volts times amperes equals watts.

Weber—Unit of magnetic flux. The magnetic flux which, linking a circuit of one turn, produces in it an electromotive force of one volt as it is reduced to zero at a uniform rate in one second.

Light, velocity of—Light waves travel at 300,000 kilometres per second (approximately). Also the velocity of radio waves.

Sound, velocity of—Sound waves travel at 332 metres per second in air (approximately) at sea level.

DECIMAL MULTIPLIERS

Prefix	*Symbol*	*Multiplier*
tera	T	10^{12}
giga	G	10^{9}
mega	M	10^{6}
kilo	k	10^{3}
hecto	h	10^{2}
deka	da	10
deci	d	10^{-1}
centi	c	10^{-2}
milli	m	10^{-3}
micro	μ	10^{-6}
nano	n	10^{-9}
pico	p	10^{-12}
femto	f	10^{-15}
atto	a	10^{-18}

FORCE

The unit of force is the newton, which is that force which, applied to a mass of one kilogram, gives it an acceleration of one metre per second per second.

1 dyne	$= 10^{-5}$ newton
1 poundal	$= 0{\cdot}13826$ newton
1 pound force	$= 4{\cdot}4482$ newtons
1 kilogram force	$= 9{\cdot}8067$ newtons
1 ton force	$= 9{\cdot}9640$ kilonewtons

ENERGY

Energy refers to capacity for performing work, or for moving against a resistance.

1 foot-pound force	$= 1{\cdot}3558$ joules
1 foot-poundal	$= 0{\cdot}04214$ joule
1 calorie	$= 4{\cdot}1868$ joules
1 erg	$= 10^{-7}$ joule
1 British thermal unit	$= 1{\cdot}05506$ kilojoules
1 horsepower hour	$= 2{\cdot}6845$ megajoules
1 kilowatt hour	$= 3{\cdot}6$ megajoules
1 therm	$= 105{\cdot}51$ megajoules

The actual energy, kinetic energy, or dynamic energy of a moving body

$$= \tfrac{1}{2} \text{ mass} \times \text{velocity}^2$$

18

HEAT

The unit of heat is the joule, while heat flow is measured in watts.

1 calorie	$= 4 \cdot 1868$ joules
1 erg	$= 10^{-7}$ joule
1 British Thermal unit	$= 1 \cdot 05506$ kilojoules
1 therm	$= 105 \cdot 51$ megajoules
1 erg per second	$= 10^{-7}$ watt
1 British Thermal unit per hour	$= 0 \cdot 29307$ watt
1 ton of refrigeration	$= 3,516 \cdot 9$ watts

TIME

1 sidereal second $= 0 \cdot 99727$ mean solar second

1 mean solar second $= 1 \cdot 002738$ sidereal seconds

Length of seconds pendulum latitude $45° = 0 \cdot 993555$ metre ($39 \cdot 1163$ inches).

POWER

1 erg/second	$= 10^{-7}$ watt
1 foot pound/second	$= 1 \cdot 3558$ watts
1 foot poundal/second	$= 0 \cdot 04214$ watts
1 horsepower	$= 745 \cdot 70$ watts
1 metric horsepower	$= 735 \cdot 50$ watts

ELECTRICAL EQUATIONS

Amperes × volts	= watts
Joules per second	= watts
Coulombs per second	= amperes
Coulombs ÷ volts	= farads
0·7373 foot pounds per second	= 1 joule
Volts × coulombs	= joules
Horsepower ÷ 1·34	= kilowatts

DIMENSIONS OF PHYSICAL PROPERTIES

Length: metre [L].   Mass: kilogram [M].
Time: second [T].   Quantity of electricity:
coulomb [Q].   Area: square metre [L^2]
Volume: cubic metre [L^3]

Velocity: metre per second	[LT^{-1}]
Acceleration: metre per second^2	[LT^{-2}]
Force: newton	[MLT^{-2}]
Work: joule	[ML^{2}T^{-2}]
Power: watt	[ML^{2}T^{-3}]
Electric current: ampere	[QT^{-1}]
Voltage: volt	[ML^{2}T^{-2}Q^{-1}]
Electric resistance: ohm	[ML^{2}T^{-1}Q^{-2}]
Electric conductance: siemens	[M^{-1}L^{-2}TQ^2]
Inductance: henry	[ML^{2}Q^{-2}]
Capacitance: farad	[M^{-1}L^{-2}T^{2}Q^2]

Current density: ampere per metre^2
$$[L^{-2}T^{-1}Q]$$

Electric field strength: volt per metre
$$[MLT^{-2}Q^{-1}]$$

Magnetic flux: weber $\quad$ [MLT^{2}T^{-1}Q^{-1}]

Magnetic flux density: weber per metre^2
$$[MT^{-1}Q^{-1}]$$

USEFUL FORMULAE

Bias Resistor

The value of the resistor to be connected in the cathode lead for developing the required bias is

$$R_k = \frac{E_k}{I_k} \times 1{,}000 \text{ ohms}$$

where E_k = bias voltage required (volts) and I_k = total cathode current (mA).

Capacitance

The capacitance of a parallel plate capacitor can be found from

$$C = \frac{0{\cdot}0885 \, KA}{d}$$

C is in picofarads, K is the dielectric constant (air = 1), A is the area of the plate in square cm and d the thickness of the dielectric.

Dynamic Resistance

In a parallel-tuned circuit at resonance the dynamic resistance is

$$R_d = \frac{L}{Cr} = Q\omega L = \frac{Q}{\omega C} \text{ ohms}$$

where L = inductance (henries), C = capacitance (farads), r = effective series resistance (ohms), Q = Q-value of coil, and $\omega = 2\pi \times$ frequency (hertz).

Frequency—Wavelength—Velocity

(See also Resonance.)

The velocity of propagation of a wave is

$$v = f\lambda \text{ metres per second}$$

where f = frequency (hertz) and λ = wavelength (metres).

For electromagnetic waves in free space the velocity of propagation v is approximately 3×10^8 m/sec, and if f is expressed in kilohertz and λ in metres

$$f = \frac{300{,}000}{\lambda} \text{ kilohertz} \qquad f = \frac{300}{\lambda} \text{ megahertz}$$

or

$$\lambda = \frac{300,000}{f} \text{ metres}$$

f in kilohertz

$$\lambda = \frac{300}{f} \text{ metres}$$

f in megahertz.

Horizon Distance

Horizon distance can be calculated from the formula

$$S = 1 \cdot 42 \sqrt{H}$$

where S = distance in miles and H = height in feet above sea level.

Impedance

The impedance of a circuit comprising inductance, capacitance and resistance in series is

$$Z = \sqrt{R^2 + \left(\omega L - \frac{1}{\omega C}\right)^2}$$

where R = resistance (ohms), $\omega = 2\pi \times$ frequency (hertz), L = inductance (henries), and C = capacitance (farads).

Inductance of Single Layer Coils

$$L \text{ (in microhenries)} = \frac{a^2 N^2}{9a + 10l} \text{ approximately}$$

If the desired inductance is known, the number of turns required may be determined by the formula

$$N = \frac{5L}{na^2}\left[1 + \sqrt{\left(1 + \frac{0 \cdot 36 n^2 a^3}{L}\right)}\right]$$

where N = number of turns, a = radius of coil in inches, n = number of turns per inch, L = inductance in microhenries (μH) and l = length of coil in inches.

Meter Conversions

Increasing Range of Ammeters or Milliammeters

Current range of meter can be increased by connecting a shunt resistance across meter terminals. If R_m is the resistance of the meter; R_s the value of the shunt resistance and n the number of times it is wished to multiply the scale reading, then

$$R_s = \frac{R_m}{(n-1)}.$$

Increasing Range of Voltmeters

Voltage range of meter can be increased by connecting resistance in series with it. If this series resistance is R_s and R_m and n as before, then

$$R_s = R_m \times (n-1).$$

Negative Feedback

Voltage Feedback

$$\text{Gain with feedback} = \frac{A}{1 + Ab}$$

where A is the original gain of the amplifier section over which feedback is applied (including the output transformer if included) and b is the fraction of the output voltage fed back.

$$\text{Distortion with feedback} = \frac{d}{1 + Ab} \text{ approximately}$$

where d is the original distortion of the amplifier.

$$\text{Effective output impedance} = \frac{R_a}{1 + \mu b}$$

where μ is the amplification factor of the output valve and R_a its anode resistance.

Current Feedback

This form of feedback may be obtained by omitting the bypass capacitor across the cathode bias resistor. Current feedback results in an increase of effective output impedance and is not recommended for output stages.

Ohm's Law

$$I = \frac{E}{R} \qquad E = IR \qquad R = \frac{E}{I}$$

where I = current (amperes), E = voltage (volts), and R = resistance (ohms).

Power

In a d.c. circuit the power developed is given by

$$W = EI = \frac{E^2}{R} = I^2R \text{ watts}$$

where E = voltage (volts), I = current (amperes), and R = resistance (ohms).

Q

The Q value of an inductance is given by

$$Q = \frac{\omega L}{R}$$

Reactance

The reactance of an inductor and a capacitor respectively is given by

$$X_L = \omega L \text{ ohms} \qquad X_C = \frac{1}{\omega C} \text{ ohms}$$

where $\omega = 2\pi \times$ frequency (hertz), L = inductance (henries), and C = capacitance (farads).
The total resistance of an inductance and a capacitance in series is $X_L - X_C$.

Resonance

The resonant frequency of a tuned circuit is given by

$$f = \frac{1}{2\pi\sqrt{LC}} \text{ hertz}$$

where L = inductance (henries), and C = capacitance (farads).
If L is in microhenries (μH) and C is in picofarads, this becomes—

$$f = \frac{10^6}{2\pi\sqrt{LC}} \text{ kilohertz}$$

The basic formula can be rearranged

$$L = \frac{1}{4\pi^2 f^2 C} \text{ henries} \qquad C = \frac{1}{4\pi^2 f^2 L} \text{ farads.}$$

Since $2\pi f$ is commonly represented by ω, these expressions can be written

$$L = \frac{1}{\omega^2 C} \text{ henries} \qquad C = \frac{1}{\omega^2 L} \text{ farads.}$$

Time Constant

For a combination of inductance and resistance in series the time constant (i.e. the time required for the current to reach 63% of its final value) is given by

$$t = \frac{L}{R} \text{ seconds}$$

where L = inductance (henries), and R = resistance (ohms).

For a combination of capacitance and resistance in series the time constant (i.e. the time required for the voltage across the capacitance to reach $1/\varepsilon$ or 63% of its final value) is given by

$$t = CR \text{ seconds}$$

where C = capacitance (farads), and R = resistance (ohms).

Transformer Ratios

The ratio of a transformer refers to the ratio of the number of turns in one winding to the number of turns in the other winding. To avoid confusion it is always desirable to state in which sense the ratio is being expressed: e.g. the 'primary-to-secondary' ratio n_p/n_s. The turns ratio is related to the impedance ratio thus

$$\frac{n_p}{n_s} = \sqrt{\frac{Z_p}{Z_s}}$$

where n_p = number of primary turns, n_s = number of secondary turns, Z_p = impedance of primary (ohms), and Z_s = impedance of secondary (ohms).

Valve Characteristics

Amplification Factor (μ) = Valve Anode Resistance (R_a) × Mutual Conductance (g_m), R_a being measured in thousands of ohms and g_m measured in mA per volt.

Alternatively

$$g_m = \frac{\mu}{R_a} \qquad R_a = \frac{\mu}{g_m}$$

Stage Gain

$$\text{Amplification } (A) = \frac{\mu \times R_1}{R_1 + R_a}$$

where R_1 is the anode load measured in the same units as R_a. If R_1 is small compared with R_a, e.g. television r.f. stages

$$A = g_m \times R_1 \text{ (approximately)}$$

Cathode Follower

$$\text{Voltage gain } \frac{V_{out}}{V_{sig}} = \frac{\mu R_k}{r_a + R_k(1 + \mu)}$$

where μ = amplification factor of the valve, r_a = anode impedance, and R_k = cathode resistor.

The stage gain of a cathode follower will always be less than unity. When μ is large and R_k is large compared with r_a the gain will be near unity.

Wattage Rating

If resistance and current values are known,

$$W = I^2R \text{ when } I \text{ is in amperes}$$

or

$$W = \frac{\text{Milliamps.}^2}{1,000,000} \times R.$$

If wattage rating and value of resistance are known, the safe current for the resistor can be calculated from

$$\text{milliamperes} = 1,000 \times \sqrt{\frac{\text{Watts}}{\text{Ohms}}}$$

Wavelength of Tuned Circuit

Formula for the wavelength in metres of a tuned oscillatory circuit is: $1885\sqrt{LC}$, where L = inductance in microhenries and C = capacitance in microfarads.

Transformer and Magnet Formulae

$$H = \frac{NI}{l}$$

H = magnetising force, amperes/metre
N = number of turns in magnetising coil
I = current, amperes
l = magnetic path length, metres.

Permeability $\qquad B = \mu H$

where

B = flux density, tesla
μ = permeability
H = magnetising force, amperes/metre.

Resistivity $\qquad \rho = \frac{Ra}{l}$

where

ρ = resistivity, ohm metres
R = resistance, ohms
a = area, metres^2
l = length, metres.

Transformer equation $\quad E = 4 \cdot 44\, Nf\, \Phi$

where

E = induced voltage
N = number of turns
f = frequency, hertz
Φ = magnetic flux, webers.

Hysteresis loss $\rho = kvfB_{\max}^x$

where

> ρ = power loss, watts
> k = a constant for a given specimen
> v = volume of iron, metres^3
> f = frequency, hertz
> B = flux density, tesla
> x = an index between 1·5 and 2·3, often taken as 2.

Eddy loss $\rho = kt^2f^2B^2$

where

> ρ = power loss, watts
> k = a constant for a given specimen
> t = thickness of laminations, metres
> f = frequency, hertz
> B = flux density, tesla.

Maximum a.c. magnetising force $H = \dfrac{NI\sqrt{2}}{l}$

where

> H = magnetising force, amperes/metre
> N = number of turns in magnetising coil
> I = r.m.s. current, amperes
> l = magnetic path length, metres.

Incremental permeability $\mu\Delta = \dfrac{10^9 l}{8\pi^2 N\Delta^2 fa} Z$

where

$$Z = \sqrt{R^2 + \omega^2 L^2}$$
$$\omega = 2\pi f$$

from which

$$\Theta = \tan^{-1}\left(\frac{R}{\omega L}\right)$$

Θ = phase angle of complex permeability, degrees

R = resistance, ohms

ω = pulsatance (angular frequency)

l = magnetic path length, metres

$N\Delta$ = number of turns

f = frequency, hertz

L = inductance, henries

a = cross-sectional area, metre^2.

Conversion Factors

One ampere-turn per metre	$= 4\pi \times 10^{-3}$ oersted
One weber per metre^2	$= 10^4$ gauss
One weber per metre^2	$= 1$ tesla
One watt per kilogram	$= 0.454$ watt per pound
One watt per pound	$= 2.2$ watts per kilogram

RESISTOR AND CAPACITOR COLOUR CODING

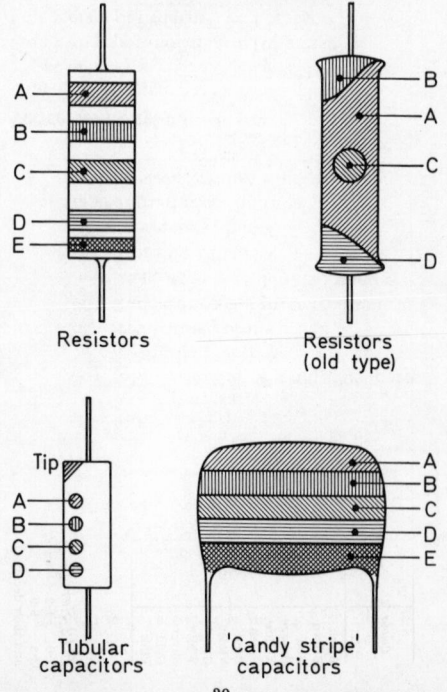

Resistors

Resistors
(old type)

Tubular
capacitors

'Candy stripe'
capacitors

RESISTOR AND CAPACITOR COLOUR CODING

Colour	Band A	Band B	Band C (Multiplier)		Band D (Tolerance)			Band E	
			Resistors	Capacitors	Resistors	Capacitors Up to 10 p.F	Over 10 p.F	Resistors	Polyester Capacitors
Black	—	0	1	1	—	2 pF	±20%	—	—
Brown	1	1	10	10	±1%	0·1 pF	±1%	—	—
Red	2	2	100	100	±2%	0·25 pF	±2%	—	—
Orange	3	3	1,000	1,000	—	—	±2·5%	—	250 v.w.
Yellow	4	4	10,000	10,000	—	—	—	—	—
Green	5	5	100,000	—	—	0·5 pF	±5%	—	—
Blue	6	6	1,000,000	—	—	—	—	—	—
Violet	7	7	10,000,000	—	—	—	—	—	—
Grey	8	8	10^8	0·01 μF	—	0·25 pF	±10%	—	—
White	9	9	10^9	0·1 μF	—	1 pF	—	—	±10%
Silver	—	—	0·01	—	—	—	—	—	—
Gold	—	—	0·1	—	—	—	—	—	—
Pink	—	—	—	—	—	—	—	Hi-Stab.	—

Note that adjacent bands may be of the same colour unseparated.

Preferred Values

E12 Series

1·0	1·2	1·5	1·8	2·2	2·7
3·3	3·9	4·7	5·6	6·8	8·2

and their decades

E24 Series

1·0	1·1	1·2	1·3	1·5	1·6	1·8	2·0	2·2
2·4	2·7	3·0	3·3	3·6	3·9	4·3	4·7	5·1
5·6	6·2	6·8	7·5	8·2	9·1			

and their decades

CAPACITANCE, RESISTANCE, INDUCTANCE

CAPACITANCE IN PARALLEL

$$C = C_1 + C_2 + C_3$$

CAPACITANCE IN SERIES

$$\frac{1}{C} = \frac{1}{C_1} + \frac{1}{C_2} + \frac{1}{C_3}$$

RESISTANCE IN PARALLEL

$$\frac{1}{R} = \frac{1}{R_1} + \frac{1}{R_2} + \frac{1}{R_3}$$

Two resistances:

$$R = \frac{R_1 \times R_2}{R_1 + R_2}$$

RESISTANCE IN SERIES

$$R = R_1 + R_2 + R_3$$

INDUCTANCE IN PARALLEL

$$\frac{1}{L} = \frac{1}{L_1} + \frac{1}{L_2} + \frac{1}{L_3}$$

INDUCTANCE IN SERIES

$$L = L_1 + L_2 + L_3$$

RESISTOR AND CAPACITOR
LETTER AND DIGIT CODE (BS 1852)

Resistor values are indicated as follows:

0·47 Ω marked	R47	100 Ω marked	100R
1 Ω	1R0	1 kΩ	1K0
4·7 Ω	4R7	10 kΩ	10K
47 Ω	47R	10 MΩ	10M

A letter following the value shows the tolerance.
F = ±1%; G = ±2%; J = ±5%; K = ±10%;
M = ±20%; R33M = 0·33 Ω ± 20%; 6K8F = 6·8
kΩ ± 1%.

Capacitor values are indicated as:

0·68 pF marked	p68	6·8 nf marked	6n8
6·8 pf	6p8	1000 nF	1μ0
1000 pF	1n0	6·8 μF	6μ8

Tolerance is indicated by letters as for resistors. Values
up to 999 pF are marked in pF, from 1000 pf to
999 000 pF (= 999 nF) as nF (1000 pF = 1 nF) and
from 1000 nF (= 1 μF) upwards as μF.

Some capacitors are marked with a code denoting
the value in pF (first two figures) followed by a multi-
plier as a power of ten (3 = 10³). Letters denote tolerance as for resistors but C = ±0·25 pf. E.g. 123 J =
12 pF × 10³ = 12 000 pF (or 0·12 μF).

Tantalum Capacitors

	1	2	3	4
Black	—	0	× 1	10 V
Brown	1	1	× 10	
Red	2	2	× 100	
Orange	3	3	—	
Yellow	4	4	—	6·3 V
Green	5	5	—	16 V
Blue	6	6	—	20 V
Violet	7	7	—	
Grey	8	8	× 0·01	25 V
White	9	9	× 0·1	3 V
			(Pink 35 V)	

TRANSISTOR AND DIODE ENCAPSULATIONS

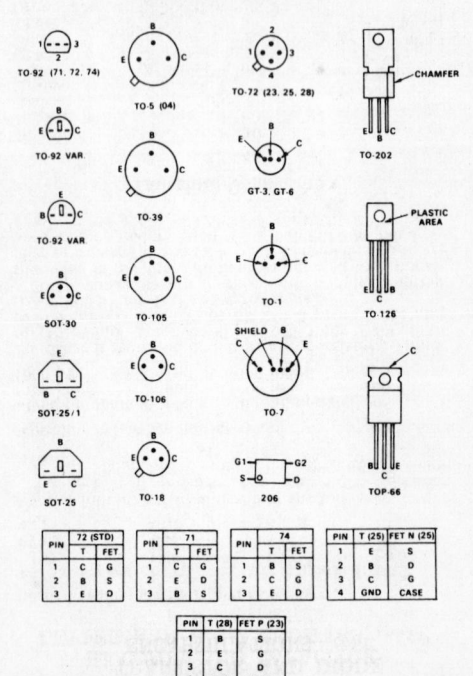

TO-92 (71, 72, 74)

TO-5 (04)

TO-72 (23, 25, 28)

TO-202 — CHAMFER

TO-92 VAR.

TO-39

GT-3, GT-6

TO-92 VAR.

TO-105

TO-1

TO-126 — PLASTIC AREA

SOT-30

TO-106

TO-7

SOT-25/1

TO-18

206

TOP-66

PIN	72 (STD)	
	T	FET
1	C	G
2	B	S
3	E	D

PIN	71	
	T	FET
1	C	G
2	B	S
3	B	S

PIN	74	
	T	FET
1	B	S
2	C	D
3	E	D

PIN	T (25)	FET N (25)
1	E	S
2	B	D
3	C	D
4	GND	CASE

PIN	T (28)	FET P (23)
1	B	S
2	E	G
3	C	D
4	GND	CASE

34

TRANSISTOR AND DIODE
ENCAPSULATIONS—*cont.*

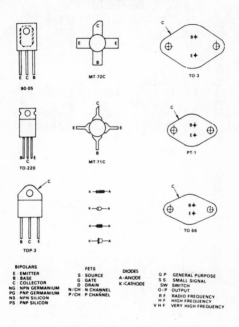

90-05

MT-72C

TO-3

TO-220

MT-71C

PT-1

TOP-3

TO 66

BIPOLARS		FETS		DIODES			
E : EMITTER		S : SOURCE		A : ANODE	G P	GENERAL PURPOSE	
B : BASE		G : GATE		K : CATHODE	S S	SMALL SIGNAL	
C : COLLECTOR		D : DRAIN			SW	SWITCH	
NG : NPN GERMANIUM		N/CH : N CHANNEL			O/P	OUTPUT	
PG : PNP GERMANIUM		P/CH : P CHANNEL			R F	RADIO FREQUENCY	
NS : NPN SILICON					H F	HIGH FREQUENCY	
PS : PNP SILICON					V H F	VERY HIGH FREQUENCY	

35

TRANSISTOR CIRCUITS AND CHARACTERISTICS

Basic Transistor Circuits Showing Signal Source and Load (R_L)	Common base	Common emitter	Common collector
CHARACTERISTICS Power Gain*	Yes	Yes (highest)	Yes
Voltage Gain*	Yes (approx. same CE)	Yes	No (less than unity)
Current Gain*	No (less than unity)	Yes	Yes
Input Impedance*	Lowest (approx. 50Ω)	Intermediate (approx. 1 kΩ)	Highest (approx. 300 kΩ)
Output Impedance*	Highest (approx. 1 MΩ)	Intermediate (approx. 50 kΩ)	Lowest (approx. 300 Ω)
Phase Inversion	No	Yes	No

* Depends on transistor and other factors

BIPOLAR TRANSISTORS

TYPE	CASE	POL MAX	Vce V/Vcb	IC mA	Vceo @ IC	hfe	@ IC mA	Ft MHz	@ IC mA	Ptot mW	Use	Comparable Types
AC107	GT3	NG	15	10	30/160	115	2	1	3	80	Low Noise Audio	AC125-2N406
AC125	TO-1	PG	12	100	10/25	100-500	2	1.3	3	125	Audio Driver	2N406
AC126	TO-1	PG	12	100	140	300	2	1.7		216	Audio Driver	
AC127	TO-1	PG	18	500	50	50	2	1.5		340	Audio O/P	AC187
AC128	TO-1	PG	16	1A	60/175	60	2	1		300	Audio O/P	AC188
AC132	TO-1	PG	12	200	115	130	2	1.3		216	Audio O/P	
AC187	TO-1	NG	15	1A	100/500	100	2	10		800	Audio O/P	AC127
AC188	TO-1	PG	15	1A	30/100	300	2	10		800	Audio O/P	AC127
AD149	TO-3	PG	30	3500	30-100	02	2	500		32W	Audio Amp.	AD161,2N2147
AD161	PT1	NG	20	3000	80-320	500	2	300		4W	Audio Amp.	AD149,2N1538,AD723
AF114	TO-7	PG	15	10	150	1A	75	015		75	H.F. Amp.	AF115,AF185,2N2127
AF115	TO-7	PG	15	10	150	1A	75			75	H.F. Amp.	AF146,AF185,2N2127
AF116	TO-7	PG	15	10	150	1A	75			75	H.F. Amp.	AF146,AF186,2N2631
AF117	TO-7	PG	15	10	150	1A	75			75	H.F. Amp.	AF139,AF197,2N4354
AF118	TO-7	PG	30	10	35	10	175			375	V.H.F. Amp.	BFX20
AS215	TO-3	NG	32	3000	45-130	500	25			30W	H.F. Sw.	OC28
AS217	TO-3	NS	32	10A	25-75	1A	22			30W	H.C. Sw.	OC29,AD138,AD723
BC107	TO-18	NS	45	100	110/450	2	10	300	10	300	H.F. Sw.	OC35,AD424
BC108	TO-18	NS	20	100	110/800	2	10	300	10	300	Low Noise, High Gain	BC207,BC147,BC182
BC109	TO-18	NS	20	100	420/800	2	10	300	10	300	S.S. Amp.	BC208,BC148,BC183
BC157	SOT-25	PS	45	100	75/260	2	10	300	10	300	S.S. Amp.	BC207,BC147,BC182
BC158	SOT-25	PS	25	100	75/500	2	10	300	10	300	S.S. Amp.	BC208,BC148,BC183
BC159	SOT-25	PS	25	100	125/500	2	10	300	10	300	Low Noise, High Gain	BC209C,BC184C,BC149C
BC177	TO-18	PS	45	100	75/260	2	10	300	10	300	S.S. Amp.	BC177,BC307,BC212
BC178	TO-18	PS	25	100	75/500	2	10	300	10	300	S.S. Amp.	BC178,BC308,BC213
BC179	TO-18	PS	20	100	125/500	2	10	300	10	300	S.S. Amp.	BC179,BC309,BC214
BC182LU	SOT-30 (TO-92/74)	NS	50	100	100/480	2	10	300	10	300	S.S. Amp.	BC157,BC307,BC212
BC183LU	SOT-30 (TO-92/74)	NS	45	100		2	10	300	10	300	S.S. Amp.	BC158,BC308,BC213
BC184(LU)	SOT-30 (TO-92/74)	NS	30	100		2	10	300	10	300	S.S. Amp.	BC159,BC309,BC214
BC186	TO-105	PS	25	200	40/200	2	10	50	10	300	Low Noise, High Gain	BC107,BC207,BC147
BC196	TO-105	PS	45	200	110/220	2	10	50	10	300	G.P. Amp.	BC109,BC209,BC149
BC207	TO-106	NS	45	200	110/450	2	10	150	10	300	S.S. Amp.	BC107,BC207,BC147
BC209	TO-106	NS	20	200	200/800	2	10	150	10	300	Low Noise, High Gain	BC109,BC209,BC149

COMMON TRANSISTOR AND DIODE DATA—*cont.*

Device	Case	PS												Application	Equivalent
BC212LU	SOT-30 (TO62/74)	PS	50	60	200	10	25	200	60-300	2	300	10	200	S.S. Amp.	BC307,BC157,BC177
BC213LU	SOT-30	PS	30	45	200	10	25	200	80-400	2	300	10	200	S.S. Amp.	BC308,BC158,BC178
BC214LU	SOT-30 (TO62/74)	PS	30	45	200	10	25	200	80-400	2	300	10	200	S.S. Amp.	
BC327	TO-92	NS	45		1000	0.7	6	100	100,000	100	800	10	100		2N3638
BC337	TO-92	NS	45		1000	0.7	6	100	100,000	100	800	10	100	S.S. Amp.	2N3642
BC547	SOT-30	NS	45	30	100	6	5	100	110,800	100	500	10	300	O/P	BC107,BC207,BC147
BC549	SOT-30	NS	30	30	100	6	5	100	110,800	150	500	10	300	O/P	BC108,BC208,BC148
BC549C	SOT-30	NS	30	30	100	5	5	100	420,800	150	500	10	300	Low Noise, High Gain	BC109,BC209,BC149
BC635	TO-92(74)	NS	45	45	1A	5	5	300	40-250	150	500	10	130	Low Noise G. Sig.	BC109C,BC149C
BC636	TO-92(74)	NS	45	45	1A	5	5	300	40-250	150	500	10	130	Low Noise, High Gain	BC640
BC639	TO-92(74)	NS	80	80	1A	5	5	130	40-160	150	500	10	130	Audio O/P	BC640
BC640	TO-92(74)	NS	80	80	1A	5	5	130	40-160	150	500	10	130	Audio O/P	MU9610,TT801
BC547		NS	45	45	200	5	5	250	100	150	350		250	Audio O/P	MU9660,TT803
BC171	TO-18	NS	45	25	200	5	5	250	100-600	150	350			Audio O/P	
BC172	TO-18	NS	20	20	200	5	5	75	50	150	350			G.P.	
BD137	TO-126	NS	60	60	1A	5	5	250	40-160	150	8W			G.P.	2N2218
BD138	TO-126	NS	60	60	1A	5	5	250	40-160	150	8W			G.P. O/P	BC212
BD139	TO-126	NS	80	80	1A	5	5	750	40-160		8W			G.P. O/P	BC212
BD140	TO-126	NS	80	80	1A	2.5	5	750	40-160		8W			G.P. O/P	BC213
BD262	TO-220	NS	60	60	4A	1.5	5	3A	750		30W			G.P. O/P	BD139
BD263	TO-220	NS	60	60	4A	1.5	5	3A	750		30W			G.P. O/P	BD140
BD266A	TO-3	NS	80	80	8A	1	5	5A	1000		60W			High Gain Darl. O/P	40409
BD264A	TO-3	NS	80	80	12A	2.5	5	5A	750		117W			High Gain Darl. O/P	40410
BD265A	TO-3	NS	80	80	12A	2.5	5	5A	750		117W			High Gain Darl. O/P	BD266
BDY20		NS	60	60	30	1	5	4A	40-185		117W			High Gain Darl. O/P	BD267
BF115	TO-72(74)	NS	30			4			60W					Power O/P	
BF167	TO-72(28)	NS	40	40	25	3		200	4		130			T.V. I.F. Amp.	
BF173	TO-72(28)	NS	25	25	25			560	37		230			T.V. I.F. Amp.	2N3055
BF177	TO-72(28)	NS	60	185	50			150	15		75			T.V. I.F. Amp.	
BF178	TO-39	NS	115	185	50			220	20		1.7W			T.V. Video Amp.	
BF179	TO-39	NS	115	250	50			120	20		1.7W			T.V. Video Amp.	
BF180	TO-72(25)	NS	20	20	20			675	13		150			T.V. Video Amp.	BF336
BF181	TO-72(28)	NS	20	20	20			750	34-140		145			U.H.F. Amp.	BF336
BF184	TO-72(74)	NS	20	20	30			220	65-220		145			H.F. Amp.	BF338
BF194	SOT-25(1)	NS	20	30	30			220	20		250			H.F. Amp.	BF338
BF200	TO-39	NS	20	100	100			650	15	3	250			H.F. Amp.	BF200
BF336	TO-72(25)	NS	180	185	60			3W	20-60		150			V.H.F. Amp.	BF195
BF337	TO-39	NS	180	185	60			3W	20-90		3W			Video Amp.	BF185
BF338	TO-39	NS	225	250	80			3W	20-60		3W			Video Amp.	BF180
BF450	TO-39	NS	35	80	1A	2		60	30	150	2.8W	50	2.8W	G.P.	

TYPE	CASE	POL MAT	Vcb	Vce	IC mA	Vceo • IC mA	hfe	Ft MHz	• IC mA	Ptot	Use	Comparable Types
BF151	TO.39	NS	30	20	25		40	50	50	50	G.P	2N4908,2N4909,2N6871
BF152	TO.39	NS	20	10A	150	150	60	50	50	50	G.P	
MJ2955	TO.3	PS	60	10A	15A	60	20-70	4	4	2.86W	Dar. O/P	TIP2955
MJ2955	TO.3	PS	60	10A	15A	60	20-70	4	4	115W	Dar. O/P	TIP2955
MJ3001	TO.3	NS	80	10A	10A	80	1000		500	150W	High Power O/P	TIP3055
MJ3001	TO.3	NS	80	10A	10A	80	1000		500	150W	High Power O/P	
MJE3055	TO.66	NS	60	4A	4A	60	20-70	2	2	90W	Power O/P	T1801
MJE3055	152	NS	60	4A	4A	60	20-70	2	2	90W	Dar. O/P	T1801
MJ6010	90.05	NS								125	Dar. O/P	T1800
MJ9661	152	PS	40	2A	2A	40	350	2		1W	Driver - O/P	AD149
MJ9661	152.01	PS	40	2A	2A	40	350	3		1W	H.C Switch	AS213
MJ9661	TO.202/05	PS	40	1.5A	1.5A	40	350	3		1W	H.C Switch	TIP3055
OC26	TO.3	PG	30	3.5A	3.5A	30	150	1		32W	H.C Switch	T1801
OC44	TO.1	PG	15	2.9		15	80-150	7.5		300W	R.F Amp	T1800
OC45	TO.1	PG	15	0.4		15	45-225	7		85	A.F O/P	2N121,AC126,2N1190
OC71	TO.1	PG	10	0.4		10	30-75	1A	1.5	85	A.F Amp	2N121,AC128,2N1190
OC72	GT.3	PG	16	0.2		16	60-150	1A		165	A.F Amp	AC127,2N2429
OC75	GT.6	PG	32	250		32	60-150	10		125	Audio O/P	AC122,2N2429
OC75	GT.6	PG	32	250		32	60-150	10		125	Audio O/P	AC125,2N2429
TIP31B	TO.220	NS	80	3A	3A	80	50	3		550	Power Amp - Sw	AC125,AC180,AC162
TIP33B	TOP.66	NS	80	10A	10A	80	1A	3	500	40W	Power Amp - Sw	AC173,AC192
TIP2955	TOP.66	PS	70	15A	15A	70	500	1	500	90W	Power Amp - Sw	AC173,AC192
TIP3055	TOP.66	NS	70	15A	15A	70	500	1	500	90W	Power Amp - Sw	
2N3054	TO.66	NS	90	4A	4A	90	25-150	3		25W	Audio O/P	MJE2955
2N3054A	TO.66	NS	90	4A	4A	90	20-100	3		25W	High Speed Sw	MJE2955
2N3055	TO.3	NS	100	15A	15A	100	20-70	8		115W	G.P Switch	AT113,OC26
2N3055	TO.3	NS	100	15A	15A	100	20-70	8		115W	Audio O/P	
2N3565	TO.105	NS	30	150	150	30	150-600	200		300	R.F - I.F Amp	BC327
2N3566	TO.105	NS	60	150	150	60	150-600	200		300	R.F - I.F Amp	BC337
2N2568	TO.105	NS	40	500	500	40	150	100		200	Low Level Amp	BC337
2N2638	TO.105	PS	40	500	500	40	20	200		300	G.P Amp & Sw	BC183
2N3638A	TO.105	PS	25	500	500	25	30	200		300	G.P Amp & Sw	BC208
2N3638A	TO.105	PS	25	500	500	25	50	100		300	G.P Amp & Sw	BC183

COMMON TRANSISTOR AND DIODE DATA—cont.

TYPE	CASE	POL MAT	Vce	Vcb	Veb @ IC mA	IC mA	Hfe @ IC mA	IC mA	Ft MHz	IC mA	Prot mW	Use	Comparable Types
2N3640	TO-105	PS	12		80	6	30-120	10	300	10	200	Saturated Switch	BC337
2N3641	TO-105	NS	60	60	500	22	40-120	150	250	10	250	G.P. Amp & Sw.	BC337
2N3642	TO-105	NS	60	60	500	22	100-300	150	250	10	350	G.P. Amp & Sw.	BC337
2N3643	TO-105	NS	45	45	500	22	100-300	150	250	20	350	G.P. Amp & Sw.	BC327
2N3644	TO-105	PS	45	45	500		115-300	50	100	20	300	G.P. Amp & Sw.	BC327
2N3645	TO-105	PS	60	60	200		60-300	50	100	20	360	G.P. Amp & Sw.	BC327
2N3702	TO-92(174)	PS	25	25	200	300	60-300	50		20	300	Saturated Sw.	BC213
2N3703	TO-92	PS	40	40	200		250-400	10		50	360	Low Level Amp	BC167A BF194
2N4250	TO-106	PS	40	40	100		250-400	10	700		310	Low Level Amp	BC559
2N4258	TO-106	PS	12	12	50	6	20-120	10	700	10	200	Saturated Sw.	
2N4033	TO-92	NS	80	40	600		100-300	100	175-	20	310	G.P.	BC307A 2N2904
2N4403	TO-92	PS	40	40	600		100	100	175-		310	H.F. Mobile R.F.	
2N5089	MT 71C	PS	18	18	600		5	250	175-	3W	15W	H.F. Mobile R.F.	
2N5591	MT 72C	NS	36	36	4A		5	500	4	10W	10W	H.F. Mobile R.F.	
2N5871	TO-3	NS	60	60	7A	4A	20-100	2.5A	100	3W	100W	Power Transistor	2N5872 2N4908 2N2955
40250	TO-66	NS	50	50	7A	1.5A	25		100	40W	20W	Power Transistor	2N3054
40408	TO-39(84)	NS	60		700	10	40-200		100	3W	3W	Power Transistor	BC639
40409	TO-39(84)	NS	80		700	10	50-250	150	100	3W	3W	Power Transistor	BD139
40410	TO-39(84)	PS	80		700	12	12	150	50			Power Transistor	BD140

FETS

FETS	CASE	BVdss V @ IC(leak)	Vgs(off) Min Max	Idss(sat) Min Max	Yfs(sat) Min Max	Poi mW	Vds	Vgs	Use/Comments
MPF102	TO-92(172)	25		2		2000	7500	15	0	N-CH Junction – VHF
MPF103	TO-92(172)	25		1		2000	5500	15	0	N-CH Junction – Audio Sw
MPF104	TO-92(172)	25		2		1500	5500	15	0	N-CH Junction – Audio Sw
MPF105	TO-92(172)	25		4		2000	7000	15	0	N-CH Junction – Audio Sw
MPF105	TO-92(172)	25		4		2500	5500	15	0	N-CH Junction – RF
2N5457	TO-92(172)	25		6		1000	5000	15	0	N-CH Junction – Audio Amp
2N5458	TO-92(172)	25		6		1500	5000	15	0	N-CH Junction – Audio Sw
2N5459	TO-92(172)	25		8		2000	5000	15	0	N-CH Junction – Audio Sw
2N5484	TO-92(172)	25		3		3000	6000	15	0	N-CH Junction – VHF
2N5485	TO-92(172)	25		4		3500	7000	15	0	N-CH Junction – VHF
BFW10	TO-72(25)	30		8			6500	15	0	N-CH Junction Audio to H.F.
BFW11	TO-72(25)	30		4			6500	15	0	N-CH Junction Audio to H.F.
MPF111	TO-72(25)	25		2	15		6500	15		N-CH Junction Audio to H.F.
MPF121		1.7			10		10000			N-CH Low MOS, VHF Amp
2N4342	TO-106	20		12		30	6000	10	0	P-CH Junction – Audio. Sw

RECTIFIERS/DIODES

TYPE	MAT	V_r	I_o (A)	V_F	●	I_f (A)	●	I_r (μA)	●	V_s	USE
A 14 F	s	1000	2.5	1.25		2.5		0.5		1000	Transient Protected (Controlled Avalanche)
A 15 A	s	1000	2.5			5				1000	G.P. Protected (Controlled Avalanche)
BY X71/L200R	s	75	.7K	1.2		25		1.1		75	Automobile H. Duty
EM 404	s	100		1						50	G.P. Rectifier
EM 401	s	100		1						100	:
EM 404	s	400		1						400	:
EM 410	s	1000		1						1000	:
IN 4001	s	50	1	1							Transient Protected (Controlled Avalanche)
IN 4002	s	100	1	1							:
IN 4003	s	200	1	1							:
IN 4004	s	400	1	1							:
IN 4005	s	600	1	1							:
IN 4006	s	800	1	1							:
IN 4007	s	1000	1	1							:
IN 5408	s	1000	3	1.25							:
IN 5059 (A14B)	s	200	3	1.25				0.2		200	:
IN 5060 (A14D)	s	400	3	1.25				0.2		400	:
IN 5061 (A14M)	s	600	3	1.25				0.2		600	:
IN 5062 (A14N)	s	800	3	1.25						800	:
MR 110	s	100						0.5			G.P. Stud Mount
MR 410	s	400						0.5			:

DIODES

DIODES	CASE	V_r	I_f (mA)	C_o (pF)	V_f	●	I_r (mA)	I_r (μA)	●	V_s	T_r (nS)	USE	COMPARABLE TYPES
Germanium													
AA 119	DO-7	30	100		2.2			10		30		AM/FM Detection	
OA 90	DO-7	30	45		1.5			10		20		Point Contact	OA70, OA80
OA 91	DO-7	90	150		1.9			10		75		G.P.—Point Contact	OA71, OA79, OA81
OA 95	DO-7	90	150		1.1			10		75		:	:
Silicon													
BA 100	DO-7	60	90							60		G.P.—Alloyed	
BA 102	DO-7	20			C_4/C_{10} = 10@0 VVV		450		50			Variable Capacitance	
BA 114	DO-7	60	20		96		180		1			Bias Stabiliser	
OA 200	DO-7	50	160		96		110		1			Small Signal—Alloyed	
OA 202	DO-7	150	160		96				1			:	
IN 914A	SD-1,-5	75	75	4	1			10		5	75	4	Small Signal—Switching	IN4148
IN 4148	DO-35	75	75	4	1			10		025	50	4	:	IN914A
5082-2800	DO-7	70	15	2	41		1		0.7	0.1	50	1	Schottky (Hot Carrier) UHF Detector, Mixer, Switch	

ZENER DATA

Voltage	400 mW types	1 W types
3·3	IN746	
3·6	IN747	
3·9	IN748	
4·3	IN749	
1·7	IN750	IN4732
5·1	IN751	IN4733
5·6	IN752	IN4734
6·2	IN753	IN4735
6·8	IN754,IN957	IN4736
7·5	IN755,IN958	IN4737
8·2	IN756,IN959	IN4738
9·1	IN757,IN960	IN4739
10	IN758,IN961	IN4740
11	IN962	IN4741
12	IN759,IN963	IN4742
13	IN964	IN4743
15	IN965	IN4744
16	IN966	IN4745
18	IN4112	IN4746
20	IN968	IN4747
22	IN969	IN4748
24	IN970	IN4749
27	IN971	IN4750
30	IN972	IN4751
33	IN973	IN4752

* Dissip. 400 mW, Op. Temp 50°C, Case DO-7 or DO-35.

† Dissip. 1 W, Op. Temp 50°C, Case DO-41. This range will dissipate up to 3 W at 75°C with 10 mm lead length as heatsink.

USING L.E.D.s

When using a light-emitting diode (L.E.D.) as an indicator, use the following formula to determine series resistance for various voltages: $R = (E - 1.7) \times 1000 \div I$; where R is resistance in ohms, E is supply voltage (d.c. !), and I is L.E.D. current in milliamps.

E.g. to operate L.E.D. at 20 mA on

6 V	use	220 ohms
9 V		390
12 V		560
24 V		1.2 k

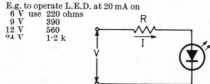

To operate a L.E.D. directly from the 240 V mains, a better scheme is to use the second circuit shown. In this, a capacitor is used as a voltage dropping element. A 1N4148 diode or similar across the L.E.D. provides the rectification required. As the voltage drop across the L.E.D. is negligible compared with the supply, capacitor current is almost exactly equal to mains voltage divided by capacitive reactance X_c.

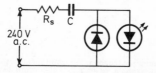

At 50 Hz, 0.47 μF will result in a L.E.D. current of about 16 mA. Resistor R_s is included to limit turn-on transients. A value of 270 ohms should be adequate.

POWER SUPPLY CONFIGURATIONS

No circuit losses are allowed for. At low voltages allow for 0·6 V diode drop.

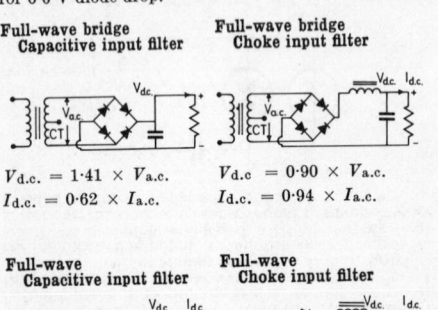

Full-wave bridge
Capacitive input filter

$V_{d.c.} = 1·41 \times V_{a.c.}$
$I_{d.c.} = 0·62 \times I_{a.c.}$

Full-wave bridge
Choke input filter

$V_{d.c} = 0·90 \times V_{a.c.}$
$I_{d.c.} = 0·94 \times I_{a.c.}$

Full-wave
Capacitive input filter

$V_{d.c.} = 0·71 \times V_{a.c.}$
$I_{d.c.} = 1·0 \times I_{a.c.}$

Full-wave
Choke input filter

$V_{d.c.} = 0·45 \times V_{a.c}$
$I_{d.c.} = 1·54 \times I_{a.c.}$

POWER SUPPLY CONFIGURATIONS—*cont.*

Half-wave
Capacitive input filter

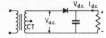

$V_{d.c.} = 1.41 \times V_{a.c.}$
$I_{d.c.} = 0.28 \times I_{a.c.}$

Half-wave
Resistive load

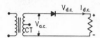

$V_{d.c.} = 0.45 \times V_{a.c.}$
$I_{d.c.} = 0.64 \times I_{a.c.}$

Full-wave bridge
Resistive load

$V_{d.c.} = 0.90 \times V_{a.c.}$
$I_{d.c.} = 0.90 \times I_{a.c.}$

Full-wave
Resistive load

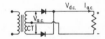

$V_{d.c.} = 0.45 \times V_{a.c.}$
$I_{d.c.} = 1.27 \times I_{a.c.}$

OP-AMP STANDARD CIRCUITS

A_v = closed loop a.c. gain f = low frequency
e_i = input voltage   −3 dB point
e_o = output voltage R_{in} = input impedance

Split supply configurations—supply connections omitted for clarity.

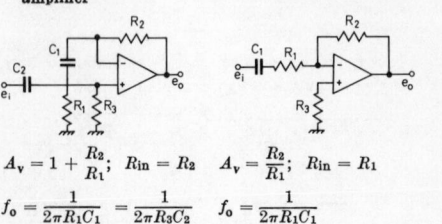

Non-inverting a.c. amplifier

$$A_v = 1 + \frac{R_2}{R_1}; \quad R_{in} = R_2$$

$$f_o = \frac{1}{2\pi R_1 C_1} = \frac{1}{2\pi R_3 C_2}$$

Inverting a.c. amplifier

$$A_v = \frac{R_2}{R_1}; \quad R_{in} = R_1$$

$$f_o = \frac{1}{2\pi R_1 C_1}$$

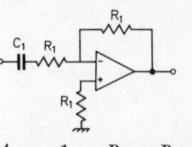

Non-inverting buffer

$$A_v = 1 \quad R_{in} = R_1$$

$$o = \frac{1}{2\pi R_1 C_1}$$

Inverting buffer

$$A_v = -1 \quad R_{in} = R_1$$

$$f_o = \frac{1}{2\pi R_1 C_1}$$

OP-AMP STANDARD CIRCUITS—cont.

Inverting summing amplifier

$$e_o = -R_A\left(\frac{e_1}{R_1} + \frac{e_2}{R_2} + \ldots + \frac{e_n}{R_n}\right)$$

$$e_o = -\frac{R_A}{R_1}(e_1 + e_2 + \ldots + e_n)$$

Difference amplifier

$$e = \left(\frac{R_1 + R_2}{R_3 + R_4}\right)\frac{R_4}{R_1} e_2 - \frac{R_2}{R_1} e_1$$

if $R_1 = R_3$ and $R_2 = R_4$ then

$$e_o = \frac{R_2}{R_1}(e_2 - e_1)$$

$$f_o = \frac{1}{2\pi R_1 C_1} = \frac{1}{2\pi(R_3 + R_4)C_3}$$

$R_2 = R_4$ for minimum offset error

Variable gain a.c. amplifier

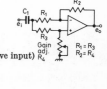

$A_v = 0$ (slider at ground)

$A_{v, max} = -\dfrac{R_2}{R_1}$ (slider at positive input)

$R_{in} = \dfrac{R_1}{2}$ (minimum)

$$f_o = \frac{1}{2\pi(\frac{1}{2}R_1)C_1}$$

47

OP-AMP STANDARD CIRCUITS—cont.

Single supply configurations—supply connections omitted for clarity.

Polarity switcher, or 4-quadrant gain control

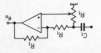

$A_v = +1$ (slider at C_1)

$A_v = 0$ (slider midposition)

$A_v = -1$ (slider at ground)

$R_{in} = \dfrac{R_1}{2}$ (minimum)

$$f_0 = \frac{1}{2\pi(\tfrac{1}{2}R_1)C_1}$$

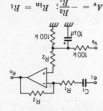

Single supply biasing of non-inverting a.c. amplifier

$$A_v = 1 + \frac{R_2}{R_1}$$

$$R_{in} = R_2$$

$$f_0 = \frac{1}{2\pi R_3 C_2} = \frac{1}{2\pi R_1 C_1}$$

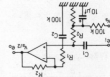

Single supply biasing of inverting a.c. amplifier

$$A_v = -\frac{R_2}{R_1}; \quad R_{in} = R_1$$

$$f_0 = \frac{1}{2\pi R_1 C_1}$$

SEMICONDUCTOR GLOSSARY

The more common terms relating to semiconductors are explained briefly here. Space naturally prevents a complete explanation and only allows for inclusion of the most common terms. For a fuller explanation see *Beginner's Guide to Transistors* by J. A. Reddihough, published by Newnes-Butterworths.

Admittance—Reciprocal of impedance, symbol Y. The unit of admittance is the *mho*.

Alpha (a)—The term used for the current gain of a transistor in the common-base mode. A term now rarely used.

Beta (β)—The current gain of a transistor in the common-emitter mode. Since the introduction of the hybrid parameters system the terms h_{fe} (the small signal current gain) or h_{FE} (the d.c. gain, which is the collector current divided by the base current) are generally used for gain in the common-emitter mode.

Bias—For a transistor to operate correctly the proper potentials have to be present at its emitter, base and collector. Normally the term bias refers to the voltage applied to the base to bring the operating point to a linear part of the amplification curve. For germanium transistors this is usually 0·3 V with respect to the emitter and for silicon transistors at least 0·6 V.

Complementary Pair—Most modern transistor audio amplifiers make use of a pair of transistors, one npn and the other pnp, with similar characteristics and closely matched gains in the driver or output stage: they are referred to as a complementary pair.

Darlington Pair—Circuit using two transistors with the collectors connected together and the emitter of the first directly coupled to the base of the second. This configuration gives very high gains—equal to the gains of the two individual transistors multiplied together.

Diac—Bi-directional voltage breakdown diode; passes current above a certain breakdown voltage. Normally employed with a triac in an a.c. control circuit.

Diode (Semiconductor)—Simple pn junction device which presents a high resistance one way around and a low resistance the other. Well known as a detector but with a wide variety of applications in all fields of electronics.

F.E.T. (Field Effect Transistor)—The f.e.t. makes use of the electric field established in a p- or n-type channel of semiconductor material to control the flow of current through the channel. The field is established by the bias applied to the gate connections and the f.e.t. is thus a voltage-controlled device. This means that it has a much higher input impedance than ordinary transistors. The main connections are the source, drain and gate but some f.e.t.s have additional connections.

Forward Bias—The biasing of a pn junction so that conduction increases. This occurs when positive connects to the p-side with negative on the n-side of the junction.

Germanium—One of the two main semiconductor elements. For it to exhibit semiconductor characteristics it must first be purified and then tri- or pentavalent impurities in minute but carefully controlled quantities added to give p- or n- type semiconductor material respectively.

Hall Effect Device—A device which, when current is passed through it, develops an e.m.f. when placed in a magnetic field.

Heat Sink—Current flow through a semiconductor device results in the production of heat. In low power devices no precautions are needed in normal operation as the heat can be dissipated by the body of the device. High power devices, however, require help in the form of a heat conductor to get rid of the excess heat. This may take the form of a fin clamped around the body but in others the body is designed to be bolted to a metal plate. Since semiconductor devices are heat sensitive the current through them increases with increase in heat. It is also necessary to take precautions when soldering a semiconductor into circuit.

hfe and hFE—See Beta.

Holding Current—Lowest current at which a thyristor-type device will continue to pass current after gate voltage has been removed.

Hybrid Circuit—Circuit employing both transistors and valves or transistors and integrated circuits.

Integrated Circuit—An integrated circuit consists of

transistors, diodes, resistors and capacitors with the necessary interconnections laid out to form a circuit such as an amplifier, bistable switch, etc. and fabricated on a single chip of semiconductor material. The chips themselves are extremely small—a fraction of the size of the encapsulation.

Leadout wires from the i.c. itself to the package pins are attached for connection of the inputs, outputs, supply voltages and any components that cannot be included such as controls, high value capacitors and inductors. These additional components are termed 'discrete components'.

Junction Capacitance—Capacitance between pn junctions in a semiconductor device. Also called barrier, depletion layer or transition capacitances (see Neutralisation).

Light Sensitive Devices—Light and heat both affect the conductivity of a pn junction. Devices are available in which a pn junction is exposed to light so as to make use of this property. Light falling on the junction liberates current carriers and allows the device to conduct.

M.O.S.T.—Type of f.e.t. with oxide insulating layer between the metal gate and semiconductor channel. It has a higher input impedance than the junction type f.e.t.

N-Type Semiconductor Material—Silicon or germanium doped with pentavalent impurity to give an excess of negative current carriers (i.e. free electrons).

Neutralisation—In radio frequency transistors there is a tendency for self-oscillation to occur due to the collector-base capacitance. In modern r.f. transistors this capacitance can be made very small. To overcome the effect in early r.f. transistors it was usual to use a small amount of capacitive negative feedback in each stage, this being known as neutralisation.

PN Junction—Junction between p- and n-type semiconductor material within the semiconductor crystal structure.

Point Contact Device—One in which the pn junction is formed at the contact between a metal 'cats-whisker' and the semiconductor material. Point contact diodes have advantages in some applications.

P-Type Semiconductor Material—Semiconductor material doped with trivalent impurity to give an excess of positive current carriers (i.e. holes).

Ratings—Specification sheets for transistors cover many facets of the device's operation but most parameters are needed only by the designer. The ratings which need to be known for replacement purposes are $V_{CE(max)}$, the maximum collector to emitter voltage; I_C the collector current; h_{fe}, the gain and f_t the cut-off frequency. The output power also needs to be observed.

Reverse Bias—Bias applied to a pn junction so as to reduce the current flow through it—positive connects to the n-type and negative to the p-type semiconductor material.

Saturation—Of a transistor when the collector current is limited by the external circuit and not by the base bias applied.

Semiconductor Device—Device whose operation is based on the use of semiconductor material. In addition to transistors and diodes there are a wide range of components which make use of semiconductor effects.

Semiconductor Material—Material whose conductive properties depend on the addition of minute quantities of impurity atoms. Pure germanium has a conductivity of about 60 ohms per cm^3 and silicon about 60,000 ohms per cm^3; semiconductors need to be about 2 ohms per cm^3. Addition of tri- or pentavalent impurities produce p- or n-type semiconductor material with an excess of positive or negative current carriers. Unlike normal conductors, semiconductors increase in conductivity with an increase in temperature.

Silicon—One of the two main semiconductor materials in use. Its energy gap ($1·08\,eV$) makes it less sensitive to heat than germanium.

Solid State Circuit—A circuit in which the current flows through solid material instead of through a gas or vacuum.

Super Alpha Pair—See Darlington Pair.

Thermal Runaway—Semiconductor materials are very sensitive to heat—germanium much more so than silicon. Circuit design has to take account of this and many components have to be included to prevent increased current flow due to heat. Without such protection heat induced current will raise the temperature leading to a further increase in current and so on, a process known as thermal runaway which can destroy a semiconductor. See Heat Sink.

Thermistor—A semiconductor whose resistance varies with temperature. Some thermistors have a negative temperature coefficient, that is resistance falls with an increase of temperature, others have a positive temperature coefficient. Used to compensate for the effect of heat in circuit operation.

Thyristor—A three-junction, four-layer semiconductor rectifier which conducts when either the voltage across it reaches a 'breakdown' point or when triggered by a pulse fed to its gate electrode. Once triggered by a pulse it remains conducting until the a.c. voltage across it reverses phase.

Triac—Bi-directional thyristor. Used in a.c. control circuitry.

Tunnel Diode—A heavily doped semiconductor diode which exhibits a negative resistance characteristic, i.e. over part of its characteristic increased forward bias leads to a reduction in the current flowing.

Type Numbers—The numbers in a transistor designation rarely describe anything about its characteristics. In the 2N series adjacent type numbers are frequently widely differing devices. European and British transistors are frequently coded with the first letter A (germanium) or B (silicon) followed by a second letter which indicates the type:

A Diode	P Photo type
C a.f. (low power)	S Switching (low power)
D a.f. (power)	U Switching (power)
E Tunnel diode	Y Diode (power)
F h.f. (low power)	Z Zener diode
L h.f. (power)	

Unijunction Transistor—Three-terminal transistor consisting of an n-type silicon bar with a base contact at each end called 'base 1' and 'base 2' and a p-type emitter region with further contact at one side. Current flow through the device from one base to the other is controlled by the current fed to the emitter. When the emitter voltage reaches a certain level, the emitter-base 1 junction virtually short-circuits. With a suitable charging circuit at the emitter the device operates as a relaxation oscillator.

Valency—The ability of atoms to unite with other atoms; due to the electrons that exist in the outer orbit, or valency band, being able to form a shared orbit with other atoms.

Varicap Diode—When reverse biased all pn junctions exhibit capacitance, since the depletion layer at the junction forms an insulator between the conductive regions. This property is exploited by the varicap diode which is used for such purposes as automatic tuning and a.f.c.

Voltage-Dependent Resistor—Resistor using semiconductor material whose resistance varies with applied voltage.

Zener Diode—Junction diode designed to operate reverse biased into the breakdown region of its characteristic. In this region large increases in current produce negligible variation in the voltage across it. Therefore it can be used for voltage stabilisation or to establish a stable reference voltage.

LOGIC TERMS

Asynchronous—Operation not dependent on clock pulses.

Buffered—Capable of driving external circuits, isolated from previous stage.

Clock—Source of regular voltage pulses, used to synchronise systems.

Dual—Two, twin.

Edge triggered—Operation of device takes place on rising (or falling) part of input pulse.

Enable—Over-ride input.

Fan-out—Number of devices that can be placed in parallel on output.

Flip-flop—Two-state device, changes state when clocked.

Hex—Six.

Latch—Retains previous input state until over-ridden.

Multiplexer—Samples many inputs in sequence, gives one output.

Octal—Eight.

One-shot—Gives single output pulse of defined duration from variable input pulse.

Open collector—TTL output which needs external pull-up resistor, can be used to wire OR outputs.

Parity—Check bit added to data, can be odd or even parity. In odd parity sum of data 1s + parity 1 is odd.

Propagation delay—Time taken for signal to pass through a device, limits highest frequency of operation.

Quad—Four.

Quiescent—Stable state not driving a load.

Schmitt trigger—Circuit with hysteresis.

Synchronous—Operation dependent on clock pulses.

LOGIC TERMINOLOGY

The logic symbols used to represent the MSI devices follow Mil Std 806B for logic symbols. MSI elements are represented by rectangular blocks with appropriate external AND/OR gates when necessary. A small circle at an external input means that the specific input is active Low, i.e., it produces the desired function, in conjunction with other inputs, if its voltage is the lower of the two logic levels in the system. A circle at the output indicates that when the function designated is True, the output is Low. Generally, inputs are at the top and left and outputs appear at the bottom and right of the logic symbol. An exception is the asynchronous Master Reset in some sequential circuits which is always at the left-hand bottom corner.

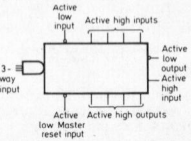

Active low input Active high inputs

3-way input

Active low output
Active high input

Active low Master reset input Active high outputs

Inputs and outputs are labelled with mnemonic letters as illustrated below. Note that an active Low function labelled outside of the logic symbol is given a bar over the label, while the same function inside the symbol is labelled without the bar. When several inputs or outputs use the same letter, subscript numbers starting with zero are used in an order natural for device operation.

Label	Meaning	
I_x	General term for inputs to combinatorial units	
J, K S, R D P	Inputs to JK, SR and D flip-flops, latches, registers and counters	
A_x S_x	Address or Select inputs, used to select an input, output, data route, junction or memory location	
$\overline{E}$	Enable, active Low on all TTL/MSI	

56

$\overline{\text{PE}}$ Parallel Enable, a control input used to synchronously load information in parallel into an otherwise autonomous circuit

$\overline{\text{MR}}$ Master Reset, asynchronously resets all outputs to zero, overriding all other inputs

$\overline{\text{CL}}$ Clear, resets outputs to zero but does not override all other inputs

CP   Clock pulse, generally a High-to-Low-to-High transition. An active High clock (no circle) means outputs change on Low-to-High clock transition

CE, CEP, CET   Count Enable inputs for counters

Z_x, O_x, F_x General terms for outputs of combinatorial circuits

Q_x General terms for outputs of sequential circuits

TC   Terminal Count output (1111 for up binary counters, 1001 for up decimal counters, or 0000 for down counters)

57

BASIC LOGIC SYMBOLS
AND TRUTH TABLES

Positive logic convention used, i.e. 1 = high, 0 = low.

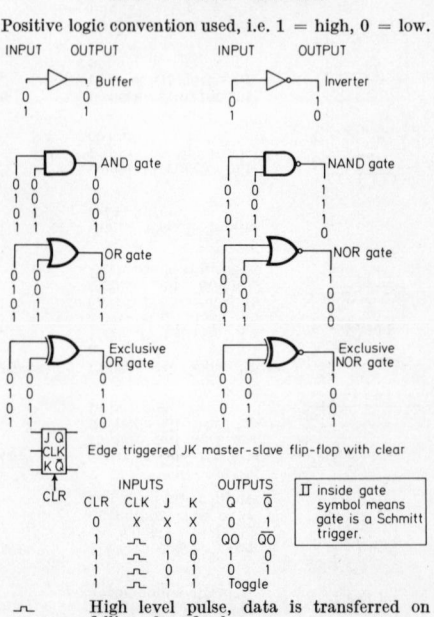

INPUT	OUTPUT		INPUT	OUTPUT
	Buffer			Inverter
0	0		0	1
1	1		1	0

AND gate

0	0	0
1	0	0
0	1	0
1	1	1

NAND gate

0	0	1
1	0	1
0	1	1
1	1	0

OR gate

0	0	0
1	0	1
0	1	1
1	1	1

NOR gate

0	0	1
1	0	0
0	1	0
1	1	0

Exclusive OR gate

0	0	0
1	0	1
0	1	1
1	1	0

Exclusive NOR gate

0	0	1
1	0	0
0	1	0
1	1	1

Edge triggered JK master-slave flip-flop with clear

Π inside gate symbol means gate is a Schmitt trigger.

INPUTS				OUTPUTS	
CLR	CLK	J	K	Q	Q̄
0	X	X	X	0	1
1	⎍	0	0	Q0	Q̄0
1	⎍	1	0	1	0
1	⎍	0	1	0	1
1	⎍	1	1	Toggle	

⎍   High level pulse, data is transferred on falling edge of pulse.

Q0   The level of Q before indicated input conditions were established.

Toggle   Each output changes to its complement on each active transition (pulse) of clock.

COMPARISON OF LOGIC FAMILIES

Since RTL was introduced in the early 1960s, there has been a steady progression in technology; the design engineer now has a wide choice of operating parameters.

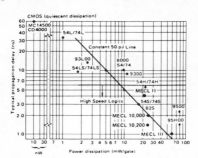

Speed/power characteristics of major logic lines

It is apparent that speed/power comparisons are not sufficient in themselves. Other important parameters to be considered are noise immunity, supply voltage requirements and fan out.

Logic family	No. of func-tions[1]	Noise immunity Volts	Prop delay[2] ns	Fan out	Max. toggle speed[2] MHz
HTL	33	5·0	110	10	3
DTL[3]	28	0·3	30	8	4
RTL[3]	39	0·3	12	5	1·5
74 series	108	0·04	9	10	15
74H series	31	0·4	6	10	40
74S series	33	0·3	3	10	125
74LS series	44	0·3	9	10	25
CMOS	100+	4·5	30	>50	10

[1] Approx. since makers vary. [2] Typical.
[3] Not recommended for new designs.

Power Supply Requirements

Each logic type has different power supply requirements and since system economics can be greatly affected by the cost of power supplies it is important to establish exact power supply parameters.

Logic family	Supply voltage			Power diss. per package mW (typ)	Decoupling and other requirements
	Nominal V	Min. V	Max. V		
HTL	15·0	14·0	16·0	60	No special precautions
RTL	3·6	3·24	3·96	20	No special precautions
DTL	5·0	4·5	5·5	30	No special precautions
74 Series	5·0	4·75	5·25	40	0·1 μF
74H Series	5·0	4·75	5·25	60	ceramic capacitor for
74S Series	5·0	4·75	5·25	40	every 8 packages to
74LS Series	5·0	4·75	5·25	8	eliminate switching current spike.
CMOS	—	3·0	18·0	0·01	No special precautions

RTL and DTL have been superseded either by CMOS (up to 5 MHz) or TTL for higher speeds.

TTL Bipolar Logic

The 54 and 74 series of transistor-transistor logic is a medium speed family of saturating i.c. logic designed for general digital applications using clock frequencies to 30 MHz and switching speeds in the 7–11 ns range under moderate capacitive loading.

The circuits are identified by a multiple emitter input transistor and an active 'pull up' in the upper output network. Clamp diodes at each input limit the undershoot that occurs in typical system applications such as driving long interconnect wiring. The active pull-up output configuration gives low output impedance in the high output state. The resulting low impedances in both output states ensure excellent a.c. noise immunity and allow high-speed operation with capacitive loads.

Complementary MOS (CMOS)

The newest of the general-purpose logic families. Originally released by RCA (COS/MOS) and followed by Motorola (McMOS) there are now well over 100 different devices available in packages for all environments.

The following are primary design features of the whole of the COS/MOS and McMOS ranges:

Double diode protection on all inputs.
Noise immunity typically 45% of VDD, 30% of VDD minimum.
Buffered output compatible with MHTL and Low Power TTL.
Low quiescent power dissipation: 25 nW typ. per package.
Power supply voltage: 3–18 V dependent on type.
Single supply operation.
High fanout: greater than 50.
High input impedance: 10^{12} ohms typ.
Low input capacitance: 5 pF typ.

CODE CONVERSION TABLES

Dec	Octal	Hex	Binary Bit Pattern 7 6 5 4 3 2 1	ASCII Character
0	0	0	0 0 0 0 0 0 0	
1	1	1	0 0 0 0 0 0 1	
2	2	2	0 0 0 0 0 1 0	
3	3	3	0 0 0 0 0 1 1	
4	4	4	0 0 0 0 1 0 0	
5	5	5	0 0 0 0 1 0 1	
6	6	6	0 0 0 0 1 1 0	
7	7	7	0 0 0 0 1 1 1	
8	10	8	0 0 0 1 0 0 0	
9	11	9	0 0 0 1 0 0 1	
10	12	A	0 0 0 1 0 1 0	
11	13	B	0 0 0 1 0 1 1	
12	14	C	0 0 0 1 1 0 0	
13	15	D	0 0 0 1 1 0 1	
14	16	E	0 0 0 1 1 1 0	
15	17	F	0 0 0 1 1 1 1	Special Characters
16	20	10	0 0 1 0 0 0 0	
17	21	11	0 0 1 0 0 0 1	
18	22	12	0 0 1 0 0 1 0	
19	23	13	0 0 1 0 0 1 1	
20	24	14	0 0 1 0 1 0 0	
21	25	15	0 0 1 0 1 0 1	
22	26	16	0 0 1 0 1 1 0	
23	27	17	0 0 1 0 1 1 1	
24	30	18	0 0 1 1 0 0 0	
25	31	19	0 0 1 1 0 0 1	
26	32	1A	0 0 1 1 0 1 0	
27	33	1B	0 0 1 1 0 1 1	
28	34	1C	0 0 1 1 1 0 0	
29	35	1D	0 0 1 1 1 0 1	
30	36	1E	0 0 1 1 1 1 0	
31	37	1F	0 0 1 1 1 1 1	
32	40	20	0 1 0 0 0 0 0	SPACE
33	41	21	0 1 0 0 0 0 1	!
34	42	22	0 1 0 0 0 1 0	"
35	43	23	0 1 0 0 0 1 1	#
36	44	24	0 1 0 0 1 0 0	$
37	45	25	0 1 0 0 1 0 1	%
38	46	26	0 1 0 0 1 1 0	&
39	47	27	0 1 0 0 1 1 1	'
40	50	28	0 1 0 1 0 0 0	(
41	51	29	0 1 0 1 0 0 1	)
42	52	2A	0 1 0 1 0 1 0	*

Dec	Octal	Hex	Binary Bit Pattern 7 6 5 4 3 2 1	ASCII Character
43	53	2B	0 1 0 1 0 1 1	+
44	54	2C	0 1 0 1 1 0 0	,
45	55	2D	0 1 0 1 1 0 1	—
46	56	2E	0 1 0 1 1 1 0	.
47	57	2F	0 1 0 1 1 1 1	/
48	60	30	0 1 1 0 0 0 0	0
49	61	31	0 1 1 0 0 0 1	1
50	62	32	0 1 1 0 0 1 0	2
51	63	33	0 1 1 0 0 1 1	3
52	64	34	0 1 1 0 1 0 0	4
53	65	35	0 1 1 0 1 0 1	5
54	66	36	0 1 1 0 1 1 0	6
55	67	37	0 1 1 0 1 1 1	7
56	70	38	0 1 1 1 0 0 0	8
57	71	39	0 1 1 1 0 0 1	9
58	72	3A	0 1 1 1 0 1 0	:
59	73	3B	0 1 1 1 0 1 1	;
60	74	3C	0 1 1 1 1 0 0	<
61	75	3D	0 1 1 1 1 0 1	=
62	76	3E	0 1 1 1 1 1 0	>
63	77	3F	0 1 1 1 1 1 1	?
64	100	40	1 0 0 0 0 0 0	@
65	101	41	1 0 0 0 0 0 1	A
66	102	42	1 0 0 0 0 1 0	B
67	103	43	1 0 0 0 0 1 1	C
68	104	44	1 0 0 0 1 0 0	D
69	105	45	1 0 0 0 1 0 1	E
70	106	46	1 0 0 0 1 1 0	F
71	107	47	1 0 0 0 1 1 1	G
72	110	48	1 0 0 1 0 0 0	H
73	111	49	1 0 0 1 0 0 1	I
74	112	4A	1 0 0 1 0 1 0	J
75	113	4B	1 0 0 1 0 1 1	K
76	114	4C	1 0 0 1 1 0 0	L
77	115	4D	1 0 0 1 1 0 1	M
78	116	4E	1 0 0 1 1 1 0	N
79	117	4F	1 0 0 1 1 1 1	O
80	120	50	1 0 1 0 0 0 0	P
81	121	51	1 0 1 0 0 0 1	Q
82	122	52	1 0 1 0 0 1 0	R
83	123	53	1 0 1 0 0 1 1	S
84	124	54	1 0 1 0 1 0 0	T
85	125	55	1 0 1 0 1 0 1	U

CODE CONVERSION TABLES—cont.

Dec	Octal	Hex	Binary Bit Pattern							ASCII Character
			7	6	5	4	3	2	1	
86	126	56	1	0	1	0	1	1	0	V
87	127	57	1	0	1	0	1	1	1	W
88	130	58	1	0	1	1	0	0	0	X
89	131	59	1	0	1	1	0	0	1	Y
90	132	5A	1	0	1	1	0	1	0	Z
91	133	5B	1	0	1	1	0	1	1	[
92	134	5C	1	0	1	1	1	0	0	\
93	135	5D	1	0	1	1	1	0	1	]
94	136	5E	1	0	1	1	1	1	0	↑
95	137	5F	1	0	1	1	1	1	1	→
96	140	60	1	1	0	0	0	0	0	—
97	141	61	1	1	0	0	0	0	1	a
98	142	62	1	1	0	0	0	1	0	b
99	143	63	1	1	0	0	0	1	1	c
100	144	64	1	1	0	0	1	0	0	d
101	145	65	1	1	0	0	1	0	1	e
102	146	66	1	1	0	0	1	1	0	f
103	147	67	1	1	0	0	1	1	1	g
104	150	68	1	1	0	1	0	0	0	h
105	151	69	1	1	0	1	0	0	1	i
106	152	6A	1	1	0	1	0	1	0	j
107	153	6B	1	1	0	1	0	1	1	k
108	154	6C	1	1	0	1	1	0	0	l
109	155	6D	1	1	0	1	1	0	1	m
110	156	6E	1	1	0	1	1	1	0	n
111	157	6F	1	1	0	1	1	1	1	o
112	160	70	1	1	1	0	0	0	0	p
113	161	71	1	1	1	0	0	0	1	q
114	162	72	1	1	1	0	0	1	0	r
115	163	73	1	1	1	0	0	1	1	s
116	164	74	1	1	1	0	1	0	0	t
117	165	75	1	1	1	0	1	0	1	u
118	166	76	1	1	1	0	1	1	0	v
119	167	77	1	1	1	0	1	1	1	w
120	170	78	1	1	1	1	0	0	0	x
121	171	79	1	1	1	1	0	0	1	y
122	172	7A	1	1	1	1	0	1	0	z
123	173	7B	1	1	1	1	0	1	1	—
124	174	7C	1	1	1	1	1	0	0	—
125	175	7D	1	1	1	1	1	0	1	—
126	176	7E	1	1	1	1	1	1	0	—
127	177	7F	1	1	1	1	1	1	1	—

— means special characters or codes not used.

DISPLAYS

One of the oldest electronic numeric readouts is the one-of-ten display such as the NIXIE* tube. An inherent disadvantage is that the numbers within the tube are not on the same plane. The red colour of the displays is difficult to change. They are difficult to multiplex because of relatively high voltage requirements. Seven-segment displays have become popular due to their lower prices and numeral format and are available in a wide variety of size, colour and type.

Incandescent displays are made in a wide range of sizes and colours and are among the brightest available. Until recently their main disadvantage was reliability due to segment failure. New materials, packages and methods, however, have improved their reliability.

Many newer incandescent displays have all seven-segment filaments contained within a single vacuum envelope and are compatible with standard DTL and TTL voltages. Multiplexing doesn't offer much advantage in part count as each display segments requires a diode to stop sneak electrical paths.

Cold cathode displays, also known as *neon, gas discharge,* or *plasma* displays are improved nixie-type displays with 7 segments instead of 10 numeral cathodes. Red–orange and easily read, they are available up to 0·75 in high. A high anode potential makes them difficult to multiplex.

Fluorescent displays are blue-green, available to approximately 0·6 in character height, and are used primarily in imported calculators. Relatively low current and voltage needs make them easy to multiplex.

The *light-emitting diode* is a solid-state device using either gallium arsenide or gallium arsenide phosphide. The advantage lies in smaller size, more reliable operation under severe mechanical conditions, and voltage current compatibility with standard technology. LEDs are available from 0·1 to 0·8 in high and are typically red in colour; however, yellows and greens are offered at a price. Most of the 0·1 in LEDs are used in domestic hand calculators.

Liquid crystal displays are unique because they scatter, rather than generate light. There are two basic types: reflective requiring front illumination, and trans-missive requiring rear illumination. These devices have the lowest power requirements, however, they require an a.c. drive system making them difficult to multiplex.

* NIXIE is a registered trademark of Burroughs Corporation.

TTL SYMBOLS

I_{IH}—High level input current.

I_{IL}—Low-level input current.

I_{OH}—High-level output current.

I_O—Off-state output current.

I_{OS}—Short-circuit output current.

I_{CCH}—Supply current output(s) high.

I_{CCL}—Supply current output(s) low.

F_{max}—Maximum clock frequency.

t_w—Average pulse width.

V_{IH}—High-level input voltage.

V_{IL}—Low-level input voltage.

V_{T+}—Positive-going threshold voltage.

V_{T-}—Negative-going threshold voltage.

V_{OH}—High-level output voltage.

V_{OL}—Low-level output voltage.

$V_{O(ON)}$—On-state output voltage.

$V_{O(OFF)}$—Off-state output voltage.

TRANSISTOR SYMBOLS

Bipolar

C_{cb}, C_{ce}, C_{eb}—Interterminal capacitance (collector-to-base, collector-to-emitter, emitter-to-base).

C_{ibo}, C_{ieo}—Open-circuit input capacitance (common-base, common-emitter).

C_{ibs}, C_{ies}—Short-circuit input capacitance (common-base, common-emitter).

C_{obo}, C_{oeo}—Open-circuit output capacitance (common-base, common-emitter).

C_{obs}, C_{oes}—Short-circuit output capacitance (common-base, common-emitter).

C_{rbs}, C_{res}—Short-circuit reverse transfer capacitance (common-base, common-emitter).

C_{tc}, C_{te}—Depletion-layer capacitance (collector, emitter).

f_{hfb}, h_{fe}—Small-signal short-circuit forward current transfer ratio cutoff frequency (common-base, common-emitter).

f_{max}—Maximum frequency of oscillation.

f_T—Transition frequency or frequency at which small-signal forward current transfer ratio (common-emitter) extrapolates to unity.

f_1—Frequency of unity current transfer ratio.

TRANSISTOR SYMBOLS—*cont.*

G_{PB}, G_{PB}—Large-signal insertion power gain (common-base, common-emitter).

G_{pb}, G_{pe}—Small-signal insertion power gain (common-base, common-emitter).

G_{TB}, G_{TE}—Large-signal transducer power gain (common-base, common-emitter).

G_{tb}, G_{te}—Small-signal transducer power gain (common-base, common-emitter).

h_{FB}, h_{FE}—static forward current transfer ratio (common-base, common-emitter).

h_{fb}, h_{fe}—Small-signal short-circuit forward current transfer ratio (common-base, common-emitter).

h_{ib}, h_{ie}—Small-signal short-circuit input impedance (common-base, common emitter).

$h_{ie(imag)}$ or $Im(h_{ie})$—Imaginary part of the small-signal short-circuit input impedance (common-emitter).

$h_{ie(real)}$ or $Re(h_{ie})$—Real part of the small-signal short-circuit input impedance (common-emitter).

h_{ob}, h_{oe}—Small-signal open-circuit output admittance (common-base, common-emitter).

$h_{oe(imag)}$ or $Im(h_{oe})$—Imaginary part of the small-signal open-circuit output admittance (common-emitter).

$h_{oe(real)}$ or $Re(h_{oe})$—Real part of the small-signal open-circuit output admittance (common-emitter).

h_{rb}, h_{re}—Small-signal open-circuit reverse voltage transfer ratio (common-base, common-emitter).

I_B, I_C, I_E—Current, d.c. (base-terminal, collector-terminal, emitter-terminal).

I_b, I_c, I_e—Current, r.m.s. value of alternating component (base-terminal, collector-terminal, emitter-terminal).

i_B, i_C, i_E—Current, instantaneous total value (base-terminal, collector-terminal, emitter-terminal).

I_{BEV}—Base cutoff current, d.c.

I_{CBO}—Collector cutoff current, d.c., emitter open.

$I_{E1E2(off)}$—Emitter cut-off current.

I_{EBO}—Emitter cutoff current, d.c., collector open.

$I_{Ec(ofs)}$—Emitter-collector offset current.

I_{ECS}—Emitter cutoff

67

current, d.c., base-short-circuited to collector.

P_{IB}, P_{IE}—Large-signal input power (common-base, common-emitter).

P_{ib}, P_{ie}—Small-signal input power (common-base, common-emitter).

P_{OB}, P_{OE}—Large-signal output power (common-base, common-emitter).

P_{ob}, P_{oe}—Small-signal output power (common-base, common-emitter).

P_T—Total nonreactive power input to all terminals.

$r_b'C_c$—Collector-base time constant.

$r_{CE(sat)}$—Saturation resistance, collector-to-emitter.

$Re(y_{ie})$

$Re(y_{oe})$

$r_{e_1e_2(on)}$—Small-signal emitter-emitter on-state resistance.

R_θ—Thermal resistance.

T_j—Junction temperature.

t_d—Delay time.

t_f—Fall time.

t_{off}—Turn-off time.

t_{on}—Turn-on time.

t_p—Pulse time.

t_r—Rise time.

t_s—Storage time.

t_w—Pulse average time.

V_{BB}, V_{CC}, V_{EE}—Supply voltage, d.c. (base, collector, emitter).

V_{BC}, V_{BE}, V_{CB}, V_{CE}, V_{EB}, V_{EC}—Voltage, d.c. or average (base-to-collector, base-to-emitter, collector-to-base, collector-to-emitter, emitter-to-base, emitter-to-collector).

V_{bc}, V_{be}, V_{cb}, V_{ce}, V_{eb}, V_{ec}—Voltage, instantaneous value of alternating component (base-to-collector, base-to-emitter, collector-to-base, collector-to-emitter, emitter-to-base, emitter-to-collector).

$V_{(BR)CBO}$ (formerly BV_{CBO})—Breakdown voltage, collector-to-base, emitter open.

V_{RT}—Reach-through (punch-through) voltage.

y_{fb}, y_{fe}—Small-signal short-circuit forward-transfer admittance (common-base, common-emitter).

y_{ib}, y_{ie}—Small-signal short-circuit input admittance (common-base, common emitter).

$y_{ie(imag)}$, or $Im(y_{ie})$—Imaginary part of the small-signal short-circuit input admittance (common-emitter).

$y_{ie(real)}$ or $Re(y_{ie})$—Real part of the small-signal short-circuit input admittance

68

(common-emitter).

y_{ob}, Y_{oe}—Small-signal short-circuit output admittance (common-base, common-emitter).

$y_{oe(imag)}$ or $Im(y_{oe})$—Imaginary part of the small-signal short-circuit output admittance (common-emitter).

$y_{oe(real)}$ or $Re(y_{oe})$—Real part of the small-signal short-circuit output admittance (common-emitter).

y_{rb}, y_{re}—Small-signal short-circuit reverse transfer admittance (common-base, common-emitter).

Unijunction

η—Intrinsic standoff ratio.

$I_{B2(mod)}$—Interbase modulated current.

I_{EB2O}—Emitter reverse current.

I_p—Peak-point current.

I_V—Valley-point current.

r_{BB}—Interbase resistance.

T_j—Junction temperature.

t_p—Pulse time.

t_w—Pulse average time.

V_{B2B1}—Interbase voltage.

$V_{EB1(sat)}$—Emitter saturation voltage.

V_{OB1}—Base-1 peak voltage.

V_p—Peak-point voltage.

V_V—Valley-point

voltage.

Field Effect

b_{fs}, b_{is}, b_{os}, b_{rs}—Common-source small-signal (forward transfer, input, output, reverse transfer) susceptance.

C_{ds}—Drain-source capacitance.

c_{du}—Drain-substrate capacitance.

C_{iss}—Short-circuit input capacitance, common-source.

C_{oss}—Short-circuit output capacitance, common-source.

C_{rss}—Short-circuit reverse transfer capacitance, common-source.

$\overline{F}$ or F—Noise figure, average or spot.

g_{fs}, g_{is}, g_{os}, g_{rs}—Signal (forward transfer, input, output, reverse transfer) conductance.

G_{pg}, G_{ps}—Small-signal insertion power gain (common-gate, common-source).

G_{tg}, G_{ts}—Small-signal transducer power gain (common-gate, common source).

$I_{D(off)}$—Drain cutoff current.

$I_{D(on)}$—On-state drain current.

I_{DSS}—Zero-gate-voltage drain current.

I_G—Gate current, d.c.

TRANSISTOR SYMBOLS—*cont.*

I_{GF}—Forward gate current.

I_{GR}—Reverse gate current.

I_{GSS}—Reverse gate current, drain short-circuited to source.

I_{GSSF}—Forward gate current, drain short-circuited to source.

I_{GSSR}—Reverse gate current, drain short-circuited to source.

I_n—Noise current, equivalent input.

$\mathrm{Im}(y_{rs})$, $\mathrm{Im}(y_{is})$, $\mathrm{Im}(y_{os})$, $\mathrm{Im}(y_{rs})$.

I_s—Source current, d.c.

$I_{S(off)}$—Source cutoff current.

I_{SDS}—Zero-gate-voltage source current.

$r_{ds(on)}$—Small-signal drain-source on-state resistance.

$r_{DS(on)}$—Static drain-source on-state resistance.

$t_{d(on)}$—Turn-on delay time.

t_f—Fall time.

t_{off}—Turn-off time.

t_{on}—Turn-on time.

t_p—Pulse time.

t_r—Rise time.

t_w—Pulse average time.

$V_{(BR)GSS}$—Gate-source breakdown voltage.

$V_{(BR)GSSF}$—Forward gate-source break-down voltage.

$V_{(BR)GSSR}$—Reverse gate-source break-down voltage.

V_{DD}, V_{GG}, V_{SS}—Supply voltage, d.c. (drain, gate, source).

V_{DG}—Drain-gate voltage.

V_{DS}—Drain-source voltage.

$V_{DS(on)}$—Drain-source on-state voltage.

V_{DU}—Drain-substrate voltage.

V_{GS}—Gate-source voltage.

V_{GSF}—Forward gate-source voltage.

V_{GSR}—Reverse gate-source voltage.

$V_{GS(off)}$—Gate-source cutoff voltage.

$V_{GS(th)}$—Gate-source threshold voltage.

V_{GU}—Gate-substrate voltage.

V_n—Noise voltage, equivalent input.

V_{SU}—Source-substrate voltage.

y_{fs}—Common-source small-signal short-circuit forward transfer admittance.

y_{is}—Common-source small-signal short-circuit input admittance.

y_{os}—Common-source small-signal short-circuit output admittance.

TTL AND CMOS DATA

TTL data

Device	Description
7400	Quad 2-input Positive NAND Gate
7401	Quad 2-input Positive NAND Gate (open collector o/p)
7401A	Quad 2-input Positive NAND Gate (open collector o/p)
7402	Quad 2-input Positive NOR Gate (open collector o/p)
7403	Quad 2-input Positive NAND Gate (open collector o/p)
7404	Hex Inverter
7405A	Hex Inverter (open collector o/p)
7406	Hex Inverter/Buffer 30V o/p
7407	Hex Buffer 30V o/p
7408	Quad 2-input Positive AND Gate
7409	Quad 2-input Positive AND Gate
7410	Triple 3-input Positive NAND Gate
7412	Triple 3-input NAND Gate (open collector o/p)
7413	Dual 4-input Schmitt Trigger
7414	Schmitt Hex Inverter Buffer
7416	Hex Inverter/Buffer 15V o/p
7417	Hex Buffer 15V o/p
7420	Dual 4-input Positive NAND Gate
7421	Dual 4-input AND Gate
7426	Quad 2-input High Voltage Interface NAND Gate
7427	Triple 3-input NOR Gate
7428	Quad 2-input NOR Buffer (Fan Out 30)
7430	8-input Positive NAND Gate
7432	Quad 2-input OR Gate
7433A	Quad 2-input NOR Buffer 15V
7437	Quad 2-input NAND Buffer
7438A	Quad 2-input NAND Buffer 15V
7441A	BCD-to-Decimal Decoder/Nixie Driver
7442	BCD-to-Decimal Decoder
7445	BCD-to-Decimal Decoder/Driver 30V output o/c
7446A	BCD-to-Seven Segment Decoder/Driver 30V/40mA
7447	BCD-to-Seven Segment Decoder/Driver 15V/40mA
7447A	BCD-to-Seven Segment Decoder/Driver 15V/40mA
7448	BCD-to-Seven Segment Decoder/Driver
7450	Expandable Dual 2 wide, 2 i/p AND-OR-INVERT Gate
7451	Dual 2 wide, 2 i/p AND-OR-INVERT Gate
7453	Expandable 4 wide, 2 i/p AND-OR-INVERT Gate
7454	4 wide 2-input AND-OR-INVERT Gate
7460	Dual 4-input Expander
7470	Positive Edge-triggered J-K Flip Flops
7472	J-K Master-Slave Flip Flops (AND inputs)
7473	Dual J-K Master Slave Flip Flops
7474	Dual D-Type Edge Triggered Flip Flops
7475	4-bit bistable latch = Quad bistable latch
7476	Dual J-K Master Slave Flip Flops + preset and clear
7481	16-bit Active Element Memory
7482	2-bit Binary Full Addder
7484	16-Lit Active Element Memory
7485	4-bit Comparator

71

7486	Quad 2-input Exclusive Or Gate
7489	64-bit RAM (16 x 4W)
7490	Decade Counter
7491	8-bit Shift Registers
7492	Divide-by-twelve Counter
7493	4-bit Binary Counter
7494	4-bit Shift Registers (Parallel-In, Serial-Out)
7495	4-bit Right Shift, Left Shift Register
7496	5-bit Shift Registers (Dual Para-in, Para-Out)
74100	8-bit Bistable Latch
74107	Dual J-K Master Slave Flip Flop
74121	Monostable Multivibrator
74122	Monostable Multivibrator with reset
74123	Dual Monostable Multivibrator with reset
74124	Universal Pulse Generator
74138	3 line to 8 line Decoder / Demultiplexer
74141	BCD-to-Decimal Decoder / Driver
74145	BCD-to-Seven Segment Decoder / Driver 15V output
74150	16-bit Data Selector
74151	8-bit Data Selector (with strobe)
74153	Dual 4 to 1 line Data Selector 1 MPX
74154	4 line to 16 line Decoder
74155	Dual 2-to-4 line Decoder / DeMPX (totem pole output)
74156	Dual 2-to-4 line Decoder / DeMPX (open collector output)
74157	Quad 2 line to 1 line Selector
74160	Synchronous Decade Counter
74162	Synchronous Decade Counter
74163	Synchronous Binary Counter
74164	8-bit Shift Register, Serial In-Parallel Out
74165	8-bit Shift Register, Parallel In-Serial Out
74174	Hex Type "D" Flip Flop
74175	Quad "D" Flip Flop with common reset
74180	8-bit Odd / Even Parity Generator / Checkers
74181	4-bit Arithmetic Logic Unit
74182	Carry-Look-Ahead Unit
74190	Synchronous Up / Down Decade Counter (Single Clock Unit)
74191	Synchronous Up / Down 4-bit Binary Counter (Single Clock Unit)
74192	Synchronous 4-bit Up / Down Counter
74193	Synchronous 4-bit Up / Down Counter
74195	Synchronous 4-bit Parallel Shift Register with J-K inputs
74196	50Mhz Presettable Decade Counter / Latch (Bi-Quinary)
74200	256-bit Random Access Memory (RAM)

CMOS data

Device	Description
CD4000	Dual 3-Input NOR gate plus Inverter
CD4001	Quad 2-Input NOR Gate
CD4002	Dual 4-Input NOR Gate
CD4006	18-Stage Static Shift Register
CD4007	Dual Complementary Pair Plus Inverter
CD4008	4-Bit full Adder with Parallel Carry
CD4009	Hex Buffer / Converter (Inverting)

CD4010	Hex Buffer/Converter (Non-Inverting)
CD4011	Quad 2-Input NAND Gate
CD4012	Dual 4-Input NAND Gate
CD4013	Dual "D" Flip-Flop with Set/Reset
CD4014	8-Stage Static Shift Register
CD4015	Dual 4-Stage Static Shift Register
CD4016	Quad Bilateral Switch
CD4017	Decade Counter/Divider
CD4018	Presettable Divide-By-"N" Counter
CD4019	Quad AND-OR Select Gate
CD4020	14-Stage Binary Ripple Counter
CD4021	8-Stage Static Shift Register
CD4022	Divide-by-8 Counter/Divider
CD4023	Triple 3-Input NAND Gate
CD4024	7-Stage Binary Counter
CD4025	Triple 3-Input NOR Gate
CD4026	Decade Counter/Divider
CD4027	Dual J K Master Slave Flip-Flop
CD4028	BCD TO-Decimal Decoder
CD4029	Presettable Up/Down Counter
CD4030	Quad Exclusive-OR Gate
CD4035	4-Stage Parallel IN/OUT Shift Register
CD4040	12-Stage Binary Ripple Counter
CD4042	Quad Clocked "D" Latch
CD4046	Micropower Phase-Locked Loop
CD4049	Hex Buffer/Converter (Inverting)
CD4050	Hex Buffer/Converter (Non-Inverting)
CD4051	Single 8-Channel Multiplexer
CD4052	Differential 4-Channel Multiplexer
CD4054	4-Line Liquid Crystal Display Driver
CD4056	BCD-7-Segment Decoder/Driver
CD4059	Programmable Divide-by-N Counter
CD4060	14-Stage Counter and Oscillator
CD4061	256-Word X 1-Bit Static Ram
CD4066	Quad Bilateral Switch
CD4068	8-Input NAND Gate
CD4069	Hex Inverter
CD4070	Quad Exclusive OR Gate
CD4071	Quad 2-Input OR Gate
CD4077	Quad Exclusive NOR Gate
CD4081	Quad 2-Input AND Gate
CD4082	Dual 4-Input AND Gate
CD4085	Dual 2-Wide 2-Input AOI Gate
CD4086	Expendable 4-Wide 2-Input AOI Gate
CD4093	Quad 2-Input NAND Schmitt Trigger
CD4099	8-Bit Addressable Latch
CD4510	BCD UP/DOWN Counter
CD4511	BCD TO 7-Segment Decoder/Driver
CD4514	1 to 16 Decoder (Output High)
CD4515	1 to 16 Decoder (Output Low)
CD4516	Binary UP/DOWN Counter
CD4518	Dual BCD UP Counter
CD4528	Dual Retriggerable Monostable

MC14502	Strobed Hex Inverter / Buffer
MC14517	Dual 64-bit Static Shift Register
MC14521	24 State Frequency Divider
MC14522	Programmable divide by N-4 bit Counter (BCD)
MC14526	Programmable divide by N-4 bit Counter (binary)
MC14534	Real Time 5-Decade Counter
MC14536	Programmable Timer
MC14543	BCD-to-Seven Segment Latch / Decoder / Driver
MC14553	Three-Digit BCD Counter
MC14566	Industrial time base Generator

LAWS OF BOOLEAN ALGEBRA

$$A + 0 = A \qquad A \cdot A = A$$

$$A + I = I \qquad A + \overline{A} = I$$

$$A \cdot 0 = 0 \qquad A \cdot \overline{A} = 0$$

$$A + A = A \qquad A \cdot I = A$$

$$A \cdot B + A \cdot C = A(B + C)$$

$$\underline{A + B \cdot C = (A + B)(A + C)}$$

$$A \cdot B \cdot C = \overline{A} + \overline{B} + \overline{C}$$

$$\overline{A} \cdot \overline{B} \cdot \overline{C} = A + B + C$$

TTL TO CMOS
FUNCTIONALLY EQUIVALENT TYPES

TTL	CMOS		TTL	CMOS	
7400	4011		74104	4095	
7401	40107		74105	4095	
7402	4001		74107	4027	
7404	4009	4049	74110	4095	
7406	4009	4049	74111	4027	
7407	4010	4050	74121	4047	4098
7408	4081		74122	4047	4098
7410	4023		74123	4098	
7411	4073		74125	4502	
7420	4012		74126	4502	
7425	4002		74132	4093	
7427	4025		74136	4030	4070
7428	4001		74141	4028	
7430	4068		74145	4028	
7432	4071		74148	4532	
7437	4011		74150	4067	
7440	4012		74151	4051	4097
7442	4028		74152	4051	4097
7445	4028		74153	4052	
7446	4511	4055	74154	4514	4515
7447	4511	4055	74155	4555	4556
7448	4511	4055	74156	4555	4556
7449	4511	4055	74157	4019	
7450	4085		74164	4015	
7453	4086		74165	4021	
7454	4086		74166	4014	
7470	4096		74167	4527	
7472	4095		74173	4076	
7473	4027		74178	4035	
7474	4013		74179	4035	
7475	4042		74180	40101	
7476	4027		74181	40181	
7477	4042		74182	40182	
7478	4027		74190	4510	
7483	4008		74191	4516	
7485	4063		74194	40104	40194
7486	4030	4070	74195	4035	
7490	4518		74198	4034	
7491	4015	4094	74200	4061	
7493	4520		74251	4051	4097
7494	4035		74279	4044	
7495	40104	40194	74283	4008	
7499	40104	40194	74290	4518	
74100	4034		74293	4520	

USING TTL:
SOME NOTES ON THE 7400 SERIES

Maximum Ratings

Temperature range: 0–70°C (7400): −55–120°C (5400).
Supply voltage: Absolute max. 7 V. *Never* use on more than 5·5 V, or on less than 4·5 V.
Input voltage: Max. 5·5 V, best kept below 5 V. To make sure a gate recognises the level, keep to 'LO' states below 0·4 V, and 'HI' states above 2·4 V.

Unused Inputs on AND Gates and NAND Gates

Don't leave these floating, if you can help it. Switching time and noise immunity are both helped greatly by either:

(i) connecting any unused inputs to a used input—but watch that the drive capacity of the preceding gate is not exceeded.

(ii) taking the unused terminals to V_{cc} through a 1 k resistor (this is so that any incoming step which exceeds the max. input voltage meets a high enough impedance to protect the gate). One resistor will tie up to 25 such inputs.

Driving Inputs with Outputs

At low level each standard TTL output can sink current from 10 standard loads, and at high level can source into 10 or 20 standard loads.

Certain devices have special inputs/outputs and as such have a different drive capability to that mentioned. Generally though, a figure of 10 is safe to assume.

Since low-level input current is a function of the internal base resistors (nearly!), at a low level up to four inputs of the *same* NAND/AND gate can be taken as one load when tied together.

Decoupling

On layouts with several chips involved, it is helpful to decouple the supply rails every three chips or so, to preserve stability. 0·1μF is sufficient.

CMOS AND TTL PINOUTS

These are the connection diagrams for most of the common logic chips now in use. Internal logic is shown where applicable.

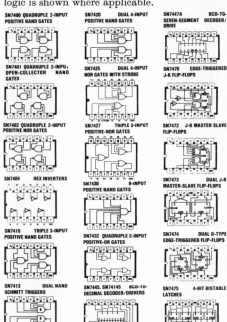

SN7400 QUADRUPLE 2-INPUT POSITIVE NAND GATES

SN7401 QUADRUPLE 2-INPU OPEN-COLLECTOR NAND GATES

SN7402 QUADRUPLE 2-INPUT POSITIVE NOR GATES

SN7404 HEX INVERTERS

SN7410 TRIPLE 3-INPUT POSITIVE NAND GATES

SN7413 DUAL NAND SCHMITT TRIGGERS

SN7420 DUAL 4-INPUT POSITIVE NAND GATES

SN7425 DUAL 4-INPUT NOR GATES WITH STROBE

SN7427 TRIPLE 3-INPUT POSITIVE-NOR GATES

SN7430 8-INPUT POSITIVE NAND GATES

SN7432 QUADRUPLE 2-INPUT POSITIVE-OR GATES

SN7445, SN74145 BCD-TO-DECIMAL DECODER/DRIVERS

SN7447A BCD-TO-SEVEN-SEGMENT DECODER/DRIVE

SN7470 EDGE-TRIGGERED J-K FLIP-FLOPS

SN7472 J-K MASTER SLAVE FLIP-FLOPS

SN7473 DUAL J-K MASTER-SLAVE FLIP-FLOPS

SN7474 DUAL D-TYPE EDGE-TRIGGERED FLIP-FLOPS

SN7475 4-BIT BISTABLE LATCHES

77

SN7476 DUAL J-K MASTER-SLAVE FLIP-FLOPS WITH PRE-SET AND CLEAR	SN7491A 8-BIT SHIFT REGISTERS	SN74122 RETRIGGERABLE MULTIVIBRATORS WITH CLEAR

SN7476 DUAL J-K MASTER-SLAVE FLIP-FLOPS WITH PRE-SET AND CLEAR

SN7491A 8-BIT SHIFT REGISTERS

SN74122 RETRIGGERABLE MULTIVIBRATORS WITH CLEAR

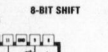

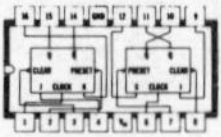

SN7480 GATED FULL ADDERS

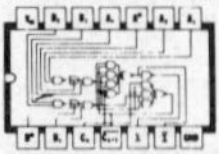

SN7481, SN7484 16-BIT ACTIVE-ELEMENT MEMORIES

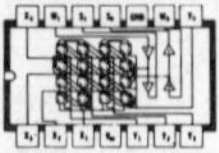

SN7485 4-BIT MAGNITUDE COMPARTORS

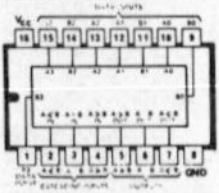

SN7486 QUADRUPLE 2-INPUT EXCLUSIVE-OR GATES

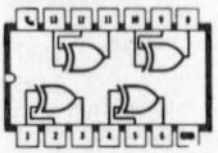

SN7489 64-BIT READ/WRITE MEMORY

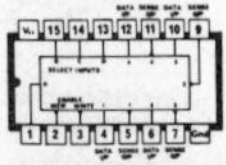

SN7490 DECADE COUNTERS

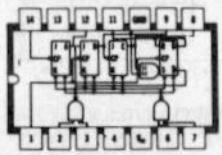

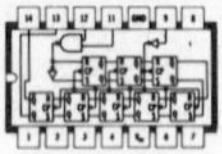

SN7492 DIVIDE-BY-TWO AND DIVIDE-BY-SIX COUNTERS

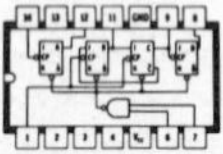

SN7492 4-BIT BINARY COUNTERS

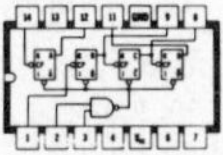

SN7495A 4-BIT RIGHT-SHIFT LEFT-SHIFT REGISTERS

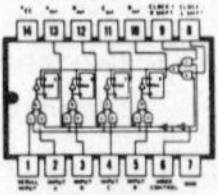

SN74104 GATED J-K MASTER-SLAVE FLIP-FLOPS

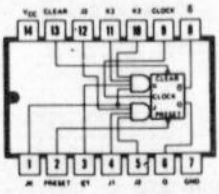

SN74121 MONOSTABLE MULTIVIBRATORS

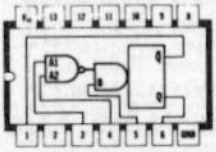

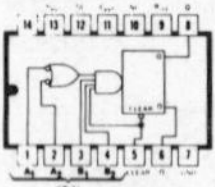

SN74160 THRU SN74163 SYNCHRONOUS 4-BIT COUNTERS

SN74160 SN74161 SYNCHRONOUS COUNTERS WITH DIRECT CLEAR
SN74162 SN74162 FULLY SYNCHRONOUS COUNTERS

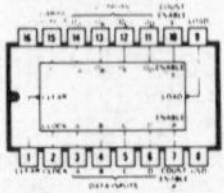

SN74164 8-BIT PARALLEL-OUT SERIAL SHIFT REGISTERS

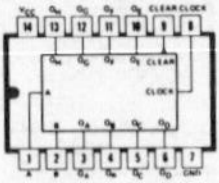

SN74165 PARALLEL-LOAD 8-BIT SHIFT REGISTERS

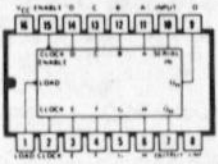

SN74174 HEX D-TYPE FLIP-FLOP

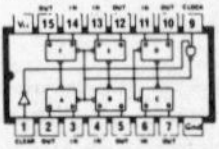

SN74175 QUAD D-TYPE FLIP-FLOP

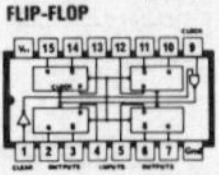

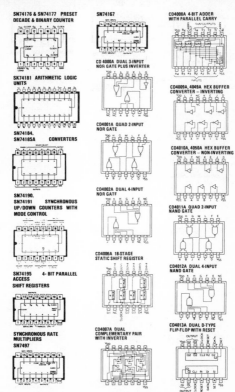

SN74176 & SN74177 PRESET DECADE & BINARY COUNTER

SK74181 ARITHMETIC LOGIC UNITS

SN74184, SN74185A CONVERTERS

SN74190, SN74191 SYNCHRONOUS UP/DOWN COUNTERS WITH MODE CONTROL

SN74195 4-BIT PARALLEL ACCESS SHIFT REGISTERS

SYNCHRONOUS RATE MULTIPLIERS SN7497

SN74167

CD 4000A DUAL 3-INPUT NOR GATE PLUS INVERTER

CD4001A QUAD 2-INPUT NOR GATE

CD4002A DUAL 4-INPUT NOR GATE

CD4006A 18-STAGE STATIC SHIFT REGISTER

CD4007A DUAL COMPLEMENTARY PAIR WITH INVERTER

CD4008A 4-BIT ADDER WITH PARALLEL CARRY

CD4009A, 4049A HEX BUFFER CONVERTER – INVERTING

CD4010A, 4050A HEX BUFFER CONVERTER – NON-INVERTING

CD4011A QUAD 2-INPUT NAND GATE

CD4012A DUAL 4-INPUT NAND GATE

CD4013A DUAL D-TYPE FLIP-FLOP WITH RESET

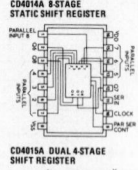

CD4014A 8-STAGE STATIC SHIFT REGISTER

CD4019A QUAD AND-OR SELECT GATE

CD4025A TRIPLE 3-INPUT NOR GATES

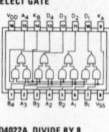

CD4015A DUAL 4-STAGE SHIFT REGISTER

CD4022A DIVIDE BY 8 COUNTER-DIVIDER

CD4027A DUAL J-K FLIP-FLOP

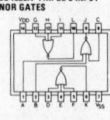

CD4016A, 4066A QUAD SWITCH

CD4023A TRIPLE 3-INPUT NAND GATE

CD4028A BCD TO DECIMAL DECODER

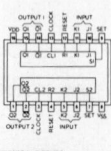

CD4017A DECADE COUNTER

CD4024A 7-STAGE BINARY COUNTER

CD4029A PRESETTABLE UP-DOWN COUNTER

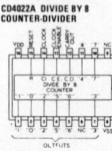

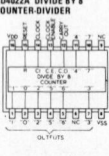

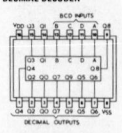

CD4018A PRESETTABLE DIVIDE-BY-N COUNTER

CD4026A DECADE COUNTER-DIVIDER

CD4030A QUAD EX-OR GATES

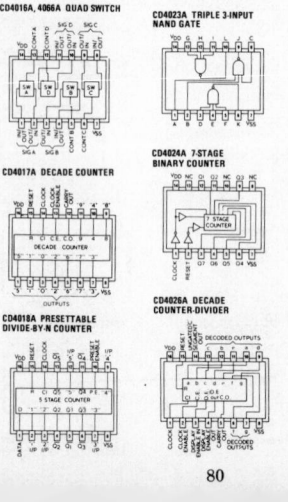

80

CD4041A QUAD TRUE COMPLEMENT BUFFER

CD4068B 8-INPUT NAND GATE

CD4077B QUAD EX NOR GATES

CD4042A QUAD D-TYPE LATCH (CLOCKED)

CD4071B QUAD 2-INPUT OR GATE

CD4081B QUAD 2-INPUT AND GATE

CD4043A QUAD 3-STATE NOR R/S LATCH

CD4072B DUAL 4-INPUT OR GATE

CD4082B DUAL 4-INPUT AND GATE

CD4044A QUAD 3-STATE NAND R/S LATCH

CD4073B TRIPLE 3-INPUT AND GATE

CD4075B TRIPLE 3-INPUT OR GATE

CD4093B GATED J-K FLIP-FLOP

CD4047A MONOSTABLE ASTABLE MULTIVIBRATOR

CD4076B QUAD D TYPE FLIP-FLOP

CD4510B BCD UP-DOWN COUNTER

81

CD4528B DUAL
RETRIGGERABLE MONOSTABLE

CD4516B BINARY UP-DOWN
COUNTER

CD4511B BCD-TO-7-SEGMENT
DECODER/DRIVER

MAINS TRANSFORMER DATA

By means of a constant obtained from the table below the turns of wire for a primary of a transformer may easily be ascertained. For example, the constant of a transformer for a supply of 220 volts 50 hertz is 1,760. Therefore, with a core of 645·16 mm² cross-sectional area use 1,760 turns of wire for primary. For a core of 1290·32 mm² use $\frac{1,760}{2} = 880$ turns, and so on. The secondary is directly proportional to the voltage ratio.

Reactive Voltage	Frequency in hertz								
	20	30	40	50	60	70	80	90	100
50	525	485	444	400	362	325	287	250	206
100	1050	975	888	800	725	650	575	500	412
110	1155	1073	976	880	797	715	632	550	453
150	1575	1455	1332	1200	1086	975	861	750	618
200	2100	1950	1775	1600	1450	1300	1150	1000	825
210	2205	2048	1864	1680	1533	1365	1207	1050	866
220	2310	2146	1952	1760	1594	1430	1264	1100	906
230	2415	2243	2041	1840	1666	1495	1321	1150	947
240	2520	2341	2130	1920	1739	1560	1378	1200	988
250	2625	2425	2220	2000	1810	1625	1435	1250	1030

DIN STANDARD CONNECTIONS

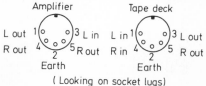

Amplifier — L out 1, L in 3, R out 4, R out 5, 2 Earth

Tape deck — L in 1, L out 3, R in 4, R out 5, 2 Earth

(Looking on socket lugs)

RESISTANCE VALUES FOR DECOUPLING AND VOLTAGE DROPPING

Current mA	Voltage dropped							
	2	5	10	20	30	40	50	60
1	2,200	4,700	10,000	22,000	33,000	39,000	47,000	56,000
2	1,000	2,700	4,700	10,000	15,000	22,000	27,000	33,000
5	390	1,000	2,200	3,900	5,600	8,200	10,000	12,000
10	220	470	1,000	2,200	3,300	3,900	4,700	5,600
20	100	270	470	1,000	1,500	2,200	2,700	3,300
50	39	100	220	390	560	820	1,000	1,200
100	22	47	100	220	330	390	470	560
200	10	27	47	100	150	220	270	330
500	3.9	10	22	39	56	82	100	120
1,000	2.2	4.7	10	22	33	39	47	56

Resistance value given to nearest preferred value. Calculate $V \times I$ to find wattage rating.

RESISTANCE VALUES FOR DECOUPLING AND VOLTAGE DROPPING—continued

Current m.A.	Voltage dropped							
	70	80	90	100	125	150	175	200
1	68,000	82,000	100,000	100,000	120,000	150,000	180,000	220,000
2	33,000	39,000	47,000	47,000	68,000	82,000	100,000	100,000
5	15,000	15,000	18,000	22,000	27,000	33,000	33,000	39,000
10	6,800	8,200	10,000	10,000	12,000	15,000	18,000	22,000
20	3,300	3,900	4,700	4,700	6,800	8,200	10,000	10,000
50	1,500	1,500	1,800	2,200	2,700	3,300	3,300	3,900
100	680	820	1,000	1,000	1,200	1,500	1,800	2,200
200	330	390	470	470	680	820	1,000	1,000
500	150	150	180	220	270	330	330	390
1,000	68	82	100	100	120	150	180	220

Resistance value given to nearest preferred value. Calculate $V \times I$ to find wattage rating.

REACTANCE OF CAPACITORS AT SPOT FREQUENCIES

	50 Hz	100 Hz	1 kHz	10 kHz	100 kHz	1 MHz	10 MHz	100 MHz
1 pF	—	—	—	—	1·6 M	160 k	16 k	1·6 k
10 pF	—	—	—	1·6 M	160 k	16 k	1·6 k	160
50 pF	—	—	3·2 M	320 k	32 k	3·2 k	320	32
250 pF	—	6·4 M	640 k	64 k	6·4 k	640	64	6·4
1,000 pF	3·2 M	1·6 M	160 k	16 k	1·6 k	160	16	1·6
2,000 pF	1·6 M	800 k	80 kΩ	8 k	800	80	8	0·8
0·01 µF	320 k	160 k	16 k	1·6 k	160	16	1·6	0·16
0·05 µF	64 k	32 k	3·2 k	320	32	3·2	0·32	—
0·1 µF	32 k	16 k	1·6 k	160	16	1·6	0·16	—
1 µF	3·2 k	1·6 k	160	16	1·6	0·16	—	—
2·5 µF	1·3 k	640	64	6·4	0·64	—	—	—
5 µF	640	320	32	3·2	0·32	—	—	—
10 µF	320	160	16	1·6	0·16	—	—	—
30 µF	107	53	5·3	0·53	—	—	—	—
100 µF	32	16	1·6	0·16	—	—	—	—
1,000 µF	3·2	1·6	0·16	—	—	—	—	—

Values above 10 MΩ and below 0·1Ω not shown. Values in ohms.

REACTANCE OF INDUCTORS AT SPOT FREQUENCIES

	50 Hz	100 Hz	1 kHz	10 kHz	100 kHz	1 MHz	10 MHz	100 MHz
1 µH	—	—	—	—	0·63	6·3	63	630
5 µH	—	—	—	0·31	3·1	31	310	3·1 k
10 µH	—	—	—	0·63	6·3	63	630	6·3 k
50 µH	—	—	0·31	3·1	31	310	3·1 k	31 k
100 µH	—	—	0·63	6·3	63	630	6·3 k	63 k
250 µH	—	0·16	1·6	16	160	1·6 k	16 k	160 k
1 mH	0·31	0·63	6·3	63	630	6·3 k	63 k	630 k
2·5 mH	0·8	1·6	16	160	1·6 k	16 k	160 k	1·6 M
10 mH	3·1	6·3	63	630	6·3 k	63 k	630 k	6·3 M
25 mH	8	16	160	1·6 k	16 k	160 k	1·6 M	—
100 mH	31	63	630	6·3 k	63 k	630 k	6·3 M	—
1 H	310	630	6·3 k	63 k	630 k	6·3 M	—	—
5 H	1·5 k	3·1 k	31 k	310 k	3·1 M	—	—	—
10 H	3·1 k	6·3 k	63 k	630 k	6·3 M	—	—	—
100 H	31 k	63 k	630 k	6·3 M	—	—	—	—

Values above 10 MΩ and below 0·1Ω not shown. Values in ohms.

SHUNTS AND RESISTANCES

SHUNTS FOR AMMETERS

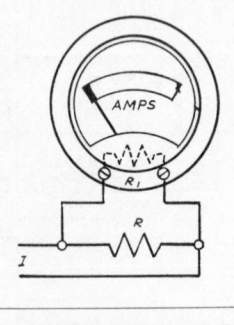

VALUE OF SHUNT
RESISTANCE

$$R = \frac{R_1 \times A}{I - A}$$

R_1 = Internal res. of meter
A = Max. reading of meter
I = Current to be measured

MULTIPLYING
POWER:

$$\frac{R_1}{R} + 1$$

SERIES RESISTANCES FOR VOLTMETERS

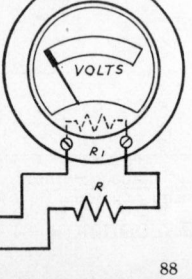

VALUE OF SERIES
RESISTANCE

$$R = \frac{E}{I} - R_1$$

R_1 = Internal res. of meter
I = Current, full scale defl.
E = Voltage to be measured

MULTIPLYING
POWER:

$$\frac{R_1 + R}{R_1}$$

KIRCHHOFF'S LAWS

(1) In an electrical circuit, at any junction where circuits branch, the algebraic sum of the currents meeting is zero.

(2) The total e.m.f. in a circuit equals the

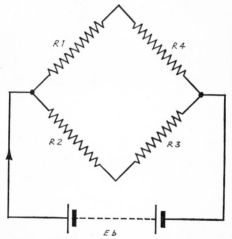

FIG. 1.—A simple series-parallel circuit, involving only an application of Ohm's Law.

sum of the resistances of its parts multiplied by the current.

Kirchhoff's Laws are in some ways closely related to Ohm's Law, but the former enable us to solve problems which we could not manage with the latter alone.

Consider Fig. 1, which shows a battery connected to a network of four resistances. Suppose it is required to find the current delivered

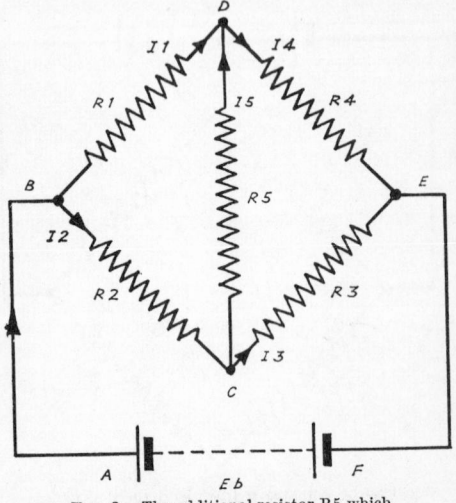

FIG. 2.—The additional resistor R5 which complicates the circuit of Fig. 1.

by the battery, the currents in each of the resistors, and the p.d. across the ends of the resistors. The problem is a very straightforward one. The resistors are in a simple series-

parallel arrangement and the problem neces-
sitates only a systematic application of Ohm's
Law and the law connecting e.m.f. and current
in a simple circuit to arrive at its solution.

Now suppose that a resistor is added to
the arrangement and it is required to find out
exactly what is occurring in the network of
five resistances shown in Fig. 2. This is not
so simple, and, in fact, Ohm's Law and its
associated formulæ are not sufficient to cope
with the problem. Attempt to work out the
problem using the methods suitable for deal-
ing with the arrangement of Fig. 2, and it will
soon be found that the fifth resistor connecting the points C and D has complicated the
matter far more than an initial comparison of
the two systems might suggest.

The problem can be solved by the application of Kirchhoff's Laws.

Kirchhoff's First Law.—The algebraic sum
of the currents meeting at a point is zero.
This is Kirchhoff's first law, and to understand
the meaning of this consider Fig. 3, where
six conductors are seen meeting at a point.
Currents are flowing along the conductors in
the directions indicated by the arrows; and
these are designated i_1, i_2, etc. It will be seen
that the current flowing into the point is
$i_4 + i_6$, and this must equal the total current
flowing out of the point,

$$i_1 + i_2 + i_3 + i_5,$$

or $(i_4 + i_6) - (i_1 + i_2 + i_3 + i_5) = 0.$

If it is agreed to distinguish a current flowing

into a point from a current flowing out of a point by assigning to the former a positive sign and to the latter a negative sign, then the currents meeting at the point in Fig. 3 are i_4 and i_6 positive, and i_1, i_2, i_3 and i_5 negative. The sum of these six currents is:

$$i_4 + i_5 - i_1 - i_2 - i_3 - i_5$$

and Kirchhoff's first law states that this sum is equal to zero, that is:

$$i_4 + i_6 - i_1 - i_2 - i_3 + i_5 = 0.$$

This is the same expression, except that the brackets are removed, as that already

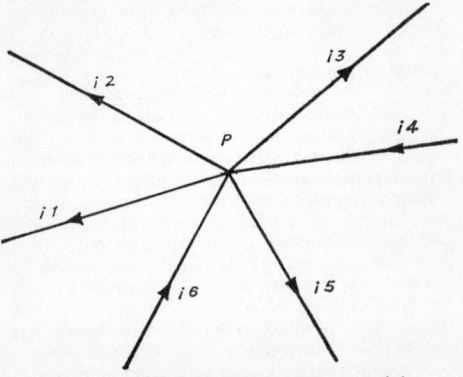

FIG. 3.—Currents flowing to and from a point, demonstrating the first law.

obtained by equating the current flowing into the point to the current leaving the point, so that the first law is simply a mathematical way of putting the self-evident fact that when several conductors meet at a point the total current entering the point is the same as the total current leaving the point.

Kirchhoff's Second Law.—In any mesh of a network the sum of the electromotive forces is equal to the sum of the products of the resistances of, and currents in, the various parts of the mesh. This is Kirchhoff's second law, and to understand its meaning go back to a consideration of Fig. 2. A mesh means a completely closed circuit and in the figure there are five such meshes: $BCDB$, $BDECB$, $FABDEF$, $FABCEF$ and $FABDCEF$. The last three of these meshes include the battery, so that the total electromotive force in each of them is the electromotive force of the battery, and the other two meshes $BCDB$ and $BDECB$ do not include the battery, and the total e.m.f. in each of them is zero. Kirchhoff's second law applied to the above-mentioned meshes gives the following equations:

For mesh $BCDB$:
$$E = I_2R_2 + I_5R_5 - I_1R_1 = 0$$
For mesh $BDECB$:
$$E = I_1R_1 + I_4R_4 - I_3R_3 - I_2R_2 = 0.$$
For mesh $FABDEF$: $E = I_1R_1 + I_4R_4.$
For mesh $FABCEF$: $E = I_2R_2 + I_3R_3.$
For mesh $FABDCEF$:
$$E = I_1R_1 - I_5R_5 + I_3R_3.$$

When working round the various meshes in a clockwise direction, a positive sign is affixed to clockwise currents and a negative sign to anticlockwise currents. A convention of this sort is an obvious necessity; clearly the product I_1R_1 is the potential difference between B and D and, since the current is flowing from B to D, the potential of D is lower than the potential of B. The product I_5R_5 is the potential difference between D and C and with the current flowing as the arrows in the figure indicate, the point C is at a higher potential than D. If, then, the change of potential from B to D is given a positive sign, it is necessary to accord a negative sign to the potential change from D to C, since this change is a rise and not a fall of potential.

Having obtained a series of equations similar to those above, it is a simple matter to solve these simultaneously and obtain the currents flowing in the various branches. The solving of simultaneous equations is a laborious though by no means difficult task, and in applying Kirchhoff's Laws to practical problems care should be taken to keep the number of unknown quantities at a minimum. The number of equations required is always the same as the number of unknowns, so that the fewer the unknowns the fewer the number of equations required. Some examples are now given, fully worked out, and a study of these should enable the reader to fully understand the method of employing, and the great importance of, Kirchhoff's Laws.

Worked Examples.—In Fig. 4 is shown a battery of e.m.f. 10 volts and negligible internal resistance connected to a network of resistances. It is required to find the battery current and the current in the various resistors.

The first thing to do in a problem of this

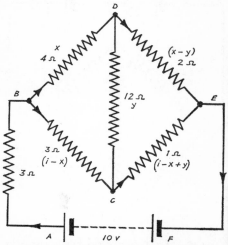

FIG. 4.—The example network solved by the application of Kirchhoff's Laws.

nature is to mark in on the diagram symbols and arrows to denote the various currents. This means an application of Kirchhoff's first law. Let the current from the battery be t, and the current out along BD be x. Then obviously the current out along BC will be $(i - x)$. In the same way let the current out along CD be designated y, so that the currents in CE and DE will be $(i - x + y)$ and

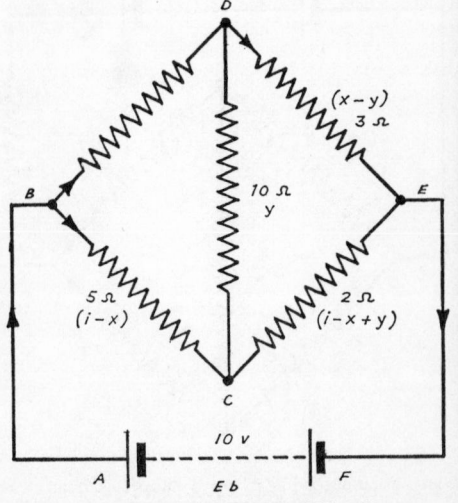

FIG. 5.—An example in which the battery has an internal resistance of 3 ohms.

$(x - y)$ respectively. These are marked on the diagram. Notice that there are only three unknown quantities, i, x and y, so that only three different equations need be found to provide a complete solution of the problem.

The reader may object at this stage and say that it is not always possible to tell at sight in which direction a particular current may flow, the arrow indicating that current may be inserted in the wrong direction. This does not matter, however, as the solution of the problem will then show this particular current with a negative sign, indicating an incorrectly marked arrow.

Having now marked off the circuit, Kirchhoff's second law is applied to form three equations from *any three meshes* in this manner:

Mesh *BD CB*—

$$E = 0 = 5x + 10y - 5(i - x)$$
$$\therefore \qquad 10x + 10y - 5i = 0 \quad . \quad . \quad (1)$$

Mesh *BECD*—

$$E = 0 = 3(x - y) - 2(-x + y) - 10y$$
$$\therefore \qquad 5x - 15y - 2i = 0 \quad . \quad . \quad (2)$$

Mesh *ABDEFA*—

$$E = 10 = 5x + 3(x - y)$$
$$\therefore \qquad 8x - 3y = 10 \quad . \quad . \quad . \quad (3)$$

These three equations can now be solved simultaneously:

$$10x + 10y - 5i = 0$$
$$5x - 15y - 2i = 0$$
$$8x - 3y = 10.$$

Eliminating i from the first and second equations gives:

$$5x - 95y = 0 \quad . \quad . \quad . \quad (4)$$

97

and combining this with the third equation gives the simultaneous

$$5x - 95y = 0 \quad 8x - 3y = 10.$$

Solving for x and y from this equation gives

$$x = 190/149 \quad y = 10/149$$

and, finally, substituting these values in any one of the first three equations gives

$$i = 400/149.$$

The complete answer to the problem is therefore as follows:

Current from battery $= i = 400/149$ amps.
Current in $BD = x = 190/149$ amps.
Current in $BC = (i - x) = 210/149$ amps.
Current in $CD = y = 10/149$ amps.
Current in $CE = (i - x + y) = 220/149$ amps.
Current in $DE = (x - y) = 180/149$ amps.

Example No. 2 is very similar to the first except that it is now supposed that the battery has internal resistance. The arrangement is shown in Fig. 5, where the internal resistance of the battery is represented by a 3-ohm resistance in one of the battery leads. The procedure of marking in symbols and arrows is just the same as the first example, and three equations are obtained from any three meshes as before.

Mesh $DECD$—
$$E = 0 = 2(x - y) - 1(i - x + y) - 12y$$
$$\therefore \qquad 3x - 13y - i = 0 \qquad . \quad . \quad (1)$$

Mesh $BDCB$—
$$E = 0 = 4x + 12y - 3(i - x)$$
$$\therefore \qquad 7x + 12y - 3i = 0 \qquad . \quad . \quad (2)$$

Mesh $FABDEF$—

$$E = 10 = 3i + 4x + 2(x - y)$$
$$\therefore \quad 6x - 2y + 3i = 10 \quad . \quad . \quad (3)$$

Eliminating i from the second and third of these equations gives

$$13x + 10y = 10 \quad . \quad . \quad (4)$$

and eliminating i from the first and third equations gives

$$15x - 41y = 0 \quad . \quad . \quad (5)$$

Solving for x and y from (4) and (5) we get

$$x = 510/683 \quad y = 20/683$$

and substituting these values in any one of the first three equations gives

$$i = 1,270/683.$$

STROBOSCOPE

A device for determining the speed of rotation of a disc, etc., by means of an interrupted light supply. In its simplest form it consists of a disc of paper or similar material around the periphery of which are arranged an equal number of light and dark segments. When illuminated by a source of light interrupted regularly (for instance, an ordinary A.C. supply), the disc will appear to remain stationary at the correct speed. The formula for determining the number of segments is $\dfrac{120 \times f}{r}$, where f is the frequency of the lighting supply and r the number of revolutions per minute. A neon lamp gives a more definite image.

DECIBEL

The decibel is one-tenth of a bel, unit of sound intensity. It is a measure of power ratio, based on logarithms to the base ten, and may be expressed as a gain or loss; it does not express absolute values, but by having a datum of reference we can express absolute values in decibels, up or down from this datum. The zero output level of 1 milliwatt in 600 ohms is frequently chosen in this country. American engineers frequently use 6 milliwatts in 600 or 500 ohms. The fact that the decibel is logarithmic means that they can be added, although the powers they represent are multiples.

If we have two powers W_1 and W_2 the gain of the second power W_2 on the first power W_1 expressed in decibels is

$$\text{Gain in decibels (dB)} = 10 \log \frac{W_2}{W_1}.$$

Although the decibel is used as a relation of power, it can also express voltage or current ratios. If the input and output resistances are equal the power ratio will be proportional to the square of the voltage or current ratio as shown below:

Let $W_2 = I_2^2 R$ $W_1 = I_1^2 R$

$\therefore$ the dB gain of W_2 on W_1

$$= 10 \log \frac{W_2}{W_1} = 10 \log \frac{I_2^2 R}{I_1^2 R}.$$

As the input and output resistances are equal

$$\text{gain in dB} = 10 \log \frac{I_2{}^2}{I_1{}^2} = 20 \log \frac{I_2}{I_1}.$$

It can also be similarly shown that, as

$$W_2 = \frac{V_2{}^2}{R} \text{ and } W_1 = \frac{V_1{}^2}{R}$$

$$\text{gain in decibels of } W_2 \text{ on } W_1 = 20 \log \frac{V_1}{V_2}.$$

The above only holds good in the case of equal input and output resistances. If the input and output resistances are equal the following is obtained:

Current Ratios with Unequal Resistance

Let $W_2 = I_1{}^2 R_2$ and $W_1 = I_1{}^2 R_1$.

Gain in dB of W_2 on W_1

$$= 10 \log \frac{I_2{}^2 R_2}{I_1{}^2 R_1} = 10 \log \left(\frac{I_2}{I_1}\right)2 + 10 \log \frac{R_2}{R_1}$$

$$= 20 \log \frac{I_2}{I_1} + 10 \log \frac{R_2}{R_1}.$$

Voltage Ratios with Unequal Resistances

$$W_2 = \frac{V_2{}^2}{R_2} \qquad W_1 = \frac{V_1{}^2}{R_1}$$

Gain in dB of W_2 on W_1

$$= 10 \log \frac{V_2{}^2/R_2}{V_1{}^2/R_1} = 10 \log \frac{V_2{}^2 R_1}{V_1{}^2 R_2}$$

$$= 10 \log \left(\frac{V_2}{V_1}\right)2 + 10 \log \frac{R_1}{R_2}$$

$$= 20 \log \frac{V_2}{V_1} + 10 \log \frac{R_1}{R_2}.$$

As $$\frac{R_1}{R_2} = \left(\frac{R_2}{R_1} \right)^{-1}$$

the above can be written as:

$$\text{dB gain} = 20 \log \frac{V_2}{V_1} - 10 \log \frac{R_2}{R_1}.$$

Example.—Calculate the current in a 600-ohm resistance in which the power dissipated is 6 dB above 1 mW.

$$\text{Gain 6 dB} = 10 \log \frac{W_2}{W_1}$$

$$0 \cdot 6 = \log \frac{W_2}{W_1}$$

or $$10^{-6} = \frac{W_2}{W_1} = \frac{W_2}{1}.$$

Therefore $W_2 = 10^{-6} \, \text{mW} = 3 \cdot 981 \, \text{mW}$.

The current flowing in the 600-ohm resistance—

$$W_2 = \frac{3 \cdot 981}{1,000} = I^2 R.$$

$$\therefore \quad I = \sqrt{\frac{3 \cdot 981}{6 \times 10}} = 0 \cdot 002575 \, \text{amp.}$$

$$= 2 \cdot 575 \, \text{mA.}$$

To convert decibels to nepers, multiply by 0·1151.

DECIBEL TABLE

The decibel figures are in the centre column: figures to the left represent decibel loss, and those to the right decibel gain. The voltage and current figures are given on the assumption that there is no change in impedance.

Voltage or current ratio	Power ratio	← − dB + →	Voltage or current ratio	Power ratio
1·000	1·000	0	1·000	1·000
0·989	0·977	0·1	1·012	1·023
0·977	0·955	0·2	1·023	1·047
0·966	0·933	0·3	1·035	1·072
0·955	0·912	0·4	1·047	1·096
0·944	0·891	0·5	1·059	1·122
0·933	0·871	0·6	1·072	1·148
0·912	0·832	0·8	1·096	1·202
0·891	0·794	1·0	1·122	1·259
0·841	0·708	1·5	1·189	1·413
0·794	0·631	2·0	1·259	1·585
0·750	0·562	2·5	1·334	1·778
0·708	0·501	3·0	1·413	1·995
0·668	0·447	3·5	1·496	2·239
0·631	0·398	4·0	1·585	2·512
0·596	0·355	4·5	1·679	2·818
0·562	0·316	5·0	1·778	3·162
0·501	0·251	6·0	1·995	3·981
0·447	0·200	7·0	2·239	5·012
0·398	0·159	8·0	2·512	6·310
0·355	0·126	9·0	2·818	7·943
0·316	0·100	10	3·162	10·00
0·282	0·0794	11	3·55	12·6
0·251	0·0631	12	3·98	15·9
0·224	0·0501	13	4·47	20·0
0·200	0·0398	14	5·01	25·1
0·178	0·0316	15	5·62	31·6
0·159	0·0251	16	6·31	39·8
0·126	0·0159	18	7·94	63·1
0·100	0·0100	20	10·00	100·0
$3·16 \times 10^{-2}$	10^{-3}	30	$3·16 \times 10$	10^{3}
10^{-2}	10^{-4}	40	10^{2}	10^{4}
$3·16 \times 10^{-3}$	10^{-5}	50	$3·16 \times 10^{2}$	10^{5}
10^{-3}	10^{-6}	60	10^{3}	10^{6}
$3·16 \times 10^{-4}$	10^{-7}	70	$3·16 \times 10^{3}$	10^{7}
10^{-4}	10^{-8}	80	10^{4}	10^{8}
$3·16 \times 10^{-5}$	10^{-9}	90	$3·16 \times 10^{4}$	10^{9}
10^{-5}	10^{-10}	100	10^{5}	10^{10}
$3·16 \times 10^{-6}$	10^{-11}	110	$3·16 \times 10^{5}$	10^{11}
10^{-6}	10^{-12}	120	10^{6}	10^{12}

LAWS

Ampere's Rule.—Refers to the deflection direction of a magnetic pointer that is influenced by a current; an analogy being that if a person is assumed to be swimming with the current and facing the indicator, the north-seeking pole is deflected towards the left hand, the south pole being deflected in an opposite direction.

Ampere's Theorem.—The magnetic field from current flowing in a circuit is equivalent to that due to a simple magnetic shell, the outer edge coinciding with the electrical conductor with such strength that it equals that current strength.

Baur's Constant.—That voltage necessary to cause a discharge through a determined insulating material 1 mm thick. The law of dielectric strength is that breakdown voltage necessary to cause a discharge through a substance proportional to a 2/3 power of its thickness.

Coulomb's Law.—Implies that the mechanical force between two charged bodies is directly proportionate to the charges and inversely so to the squares of the distance separating them.

Faraday's Laws.—That of induction is that the e.m.f. induced in a circuit is proportional to the rate of change in the lines of force linking it. That of electrolysis is (1) That the quantity of a substance deposited in defined time is proportional to the current. (2) That different substances and quantities deposited by a single current in a similar time are proportional to the electro-chemical equivalents. The Faraday Effect states that when a light beam passes through a strong magnetic field the plane of polarisation is rotated.

Fleming's Rule.—By placing the thumb and two fingers at right-angles, respectively, the forefinger can represent the direction of magnetic force lines; the second finger, current direction; the thumb, motion direction.

Hall Effect.—If an electric current flows across the lines of flux of a magnetic field, an e.m.f. is observed at right-angles to the primary current and to the magnetic field. When a steady current flows in a magnetic field, e.m.f. tendencies develop at right-angles to the magnetic force and to the current, proportionately to the product of the current strength, the magnetic force and the sine of the angle between the direction of quantities.

Joule's Law.—As a formula this is I^2Rt joules. It refers to that heat developed by the current (I) which is proportional to the square of I multiplied by R and t, letting $R =$ resistance and $t =$ time. If the formula is seen as $JH = RI^2t$ it equals EIt, letting $J =$ joules equivalent of heat, and $H =$ the number of heat units.

Kerr Effect.—Illustrates that an angle of rotation is proportional to a magnetisation intensity and applies to the rotation of polarisation plane of plain polarised light as reflected from the pole of a magnet. The number (a constant) varies for different wavelengths and specific materials, making necessary the multiplication of magnetisation intensity in order to find the angle of rotation forming the effect.

Lenz's Law.—That induced currents have such a direction that the reaction forces generated have a tendency to oppose the motion or action producing them.

Maxwell's Law.—(a) Any two circuits carrying current tend so to dispose themselves as to include the largest possible number of lines of force common to the two. (b) Every electro-magnetic system tends to change its configuration so that the exciting circuit will embrace the largest number of lines of force in a positive direction.

Maxwell's Rule.—Maxwell's *unit tubes* of electric or magnetic induction are such that a *unit pole* delivers 4π unit tubes of force.

Miller Circuit.—A form of circuit in which the time-constant of a resistance-capacitance combination is multiplied by means of the Miller effect on the capacitance. Named after John M. Miller.

Miller Effect.—Implies that the grid input impedance of a valve with a load in the anode circuit is different from its input impedance with a zero anode load. Should the load in the anode be resistance, the input impedance is purely capacitative. If the load impedance has a reactive component, the input impedance will have a resistive component. In pre-detector amplification, with a.v.c. to signal grids, the capacity across the tuned grid circuits tends to vary with the signal strength, evidencing detuning, the effect causing a charge (electrostatic) to be induced by the anode on the grid.

Planck's Constant.—Quanta of energy radiated when atomic electrons transfer from one state to another, assuming both to be *energy states* with electro-magnetic radiation. The constant (h) is given the value of $6 \cdot 626 \times 10^{-34}$ joule second. h is usually coupled to the symbol (v) to represent the frequency of the radiated energy in hertz. That is, the frequency of the radiated energy is determinable by the relation $W_1 - W_2$, this equalling hv. W_1 and W_2 equal the values of the internal energy of the atom in initial and final stages. Some textbooks on radio refer to this constant as the *Quantum Theory*.

Thévenin's Theorem.—The current through a resistance R connected across any two points A and B of an active network (i.e. a network containing one or more sources of e.m.f.) is obtained by dividing the p.d. between A and B, with R disconnected, by $(R+r)$, where r is the resistance of the network measured between points A and B with R disconnected and the sources of e.m.f. replaced by their internal resistances.

107

THE IONOSPHERE

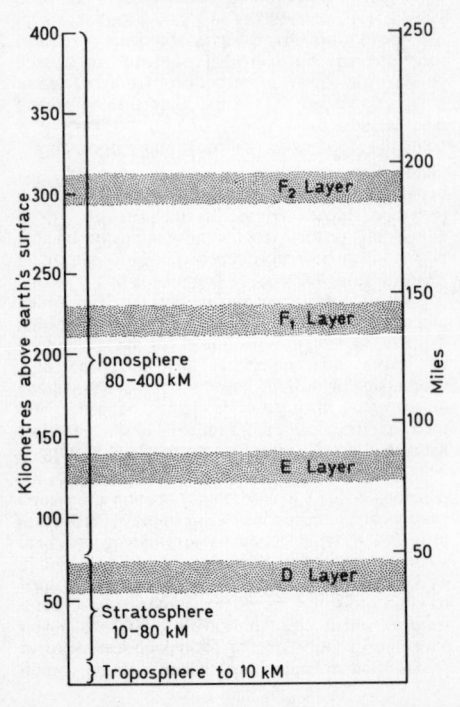

THE ELECTROMAGNETIC WAVE SPECTRUM

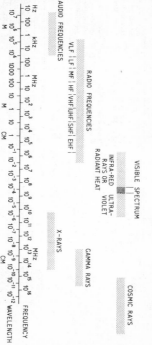

AUDIO FREQUENCIES

RADIO FREQUENCIES

VLF | LF | MF | HF | VHF | UHF | SHF | EHF |

VISIBLE SPECTRUM

INFRA-RED
RAYS OR
RADIANT HEAT

ULTRA-
VIOLET

X-RAYS

GAMMA RAYS

COSMIC RAYS

Hz   10   100   1   10   100   1   10   100   1   10   10²   10³   10⁴   10⁵   10⁶   10⁷   10⁸   10⁹   10¹⁰   10¹¹   10¹²   10¹³   10¹⁴   10¹⁵   10¹⁶

        kHz   MHz   MHz

M   10⁶   10⁵   10   1   10⁴   10³   10²   1   10¹   10⁻¹   10⁻²   10⁻³   10⁻⁴   10⁻⁵   10⁻⁶   10⁻⁷   10⁻⁸   10⁻⁹   10⁻¹⁰   10⁻¹¹   10⁻¹²

        M   CM   CM   WAVELENGTH
                                                                                          FREQUENCY

RADIO WAVEBANDS

Frequency band	Frequency	Wavelength	Waveband definition
v.l.f.	3 to 30 kHz	100,000 to 10,000 m	myriametric
l.f.	30 to 300 kHz	10,000 to 1,000 m	kilometric
m.f.	300 to 3,000 kHz	1,000 to 100 m	hectometric
h.f.	3 to 30 MHz	100 to 10 m	decametric
v.h.f.	30 to 300 MHz	10 to 1 m	metric
u.h.f.	300 to 3,000 MHz	1 to 0·1 m	decimetric
s.h.f.	3 to 30 GHz	10 to 1 cm	centimetric
e.h.f.	30 to 300 GHz	1 to 0·1 cm	millimetric
e.h.f.	300 to 3,000 GHz	0·1 to 0·01 cm	decimillimetric

THE SINPO CODE

	S	I	N	P	O
Rating scale	Signal strength	Interference (QRM)	Noise (QRN)	Propagation disturbance (QRK)	Overall readability (QRK)
5	Excellent	Nil	Nil	Nil	Excellent
4	Good	Slight	Slight	Slight	Good
3	Fair	Moderate	Moderate	Moderate	Fair
	Poor	Severe	Severe	Severe	Poor
2	Barely audible	Extreme	Extreme	Extreme	Unusable
1					

B.B.C. A.M. RADIO STATIONS

Radio 1

	kHz	m	kW		kHz	m	kW
Bournemouth	1484	202	2	Moorside Edge	1214	247	50
Brighton	1214	247	1	Newcastle	1214	247	2
Brookmans	1214	247	50	Plymouth	1214	247	1
Park				Postwick	1214	247	1
Burghead	1214	247	20	Redmoss	1214	247	2
Droitwich	1214	247	30	Redruth	1214	247	2
Fareham	1214	247	1	Torquay	1484	202	0·5
Hull	1214	247	0·15	Tywyn	1214	247	0·5
Lisnagarvey	1214	247	10	Washford	1214	247	60
Londonderry	1214	247	0·25	Westerglen	1214	247	40

Radio 2

	kHz	m	kW		kHz	m	kW
Droitwich	200	1500	400	Glasgow	1484	202	2
Dundee	1484	202	2	Redmoss	1484	202	2
Edinburgh	1484	202	2				

Radio 3

	kHz	m	kW		kHz	m	kW
Daventry	647	464	150	Newcastle	647	464	2
Dundee	1594	188	0·25	Plymouth	647	464	0·5
Edinburgh	647	464	2	Redmoss	647	464	2
Exeter	647	464	0·25	Redruth	647	464	1
Glasgow	647	464	2	Swansea	647	464	1

Radio 4

England

	kHz	m	kW		kHz	m	kW
Barnstaple*	683	439	2	Hull	908	330	2
Barrow	1052	285	2	Moorside Edge	692	434	300
Bartley	692	434	10	Plymouth*	1457	206	1
Bexhill	1052	285	2	Postwick	1052	285	7·5
Brighton	692	434	2	Ramsgate	692	434	2
Brisco	1052	285	2	Redruth*	755	397	2
(Carlisle)				Redruth	908	330	2
Brookmans	908	330	140	Scarborough	908	330	2
Park				Stagshaw	908	330	100
Clevedon	908	330	20	Start Point	1052	285	100
Cromer	692	434	2	Stockton	1052	285	2
Droitwich	1052	285	150	Swindon	1340	224	0·5
Exeter*	989	303	1	Torquay*	854	351	1
Folkestone	1052	285	1	Whitehaven	692	434	1·3

* These transmitters carry South-West Region local programmes.

111

Radio 4

Scotland

	kHz	m	kW		kHz	m	kW
Burghead	810	371	100	Redmoss	810	371	5
Dumfries	810	371	2	Westerglen	810	371	100

Wales

	kHz	m	kW		kHz	m	kW
Penmon	882	341	10	Washford	882	341	100
Tywyn	882	341	5	Wrexham	882	341	2

Northern Ireland

	kHz	m	kW		kHz	m	kW
Belfast (Divis)	720	417	0·5	Londonderry	720	417	0·25

Radio Ulster

	kHz	m	kW		kHz	m	kW
Lisnagarvey	1341	224	100	Londonderry	1341	224	0·24

B.B.C. Station Changes

On 23rd November 1978 the B.B.C. will be changing frequencies of long and medium wave transmissions. There will also be new low power transmitters for Radio 4 in some areas. The new frequencies will be:

	kHz	m		kHz	m
Radio 1	1053	285	Radio 3	1215	247
	1089	275			
Bournemouth	1485	202			
			Radio 4	200	1500
Radio 2	693	433		227	1322
	909	330	Tyneside	603	498
			Aberdeen	1449	207
			Carlisle, Dundee, Edinburgh, Glasgow	1485	202

A.M. RADIO BROADCASTING BANDS

	kHz	Metres or Metre Band
Long waves	150–285	1,053–2,000
Medium waves	525–1,605	187–571
Short waves	2,300–2,495*	120 m.b.
,,	3,200–3,400*	90 m.b.
,,	3,900–4,000	75 m.b.
,,	4,750–5,060*	60 m.b.
,,	5,950–6,200	49 m.b.
,,	7,100–7,300	41 m.b.
,,	9,500–9,775	31 m.b.
,,	11,700–11,975	25 m.b.
,,	15,100–15,450	19 m.b.
,,	17,700–17,900	16 m.b.
,,	21,450–21,750	13 m.b.
,,	25,600–26,100	11 m.b.

* Tropical broadcasting bands

Service	Station	Radio 1/2	Radio 3	Radio 4	Max. erp kW
London	Oxford	89·5s	91·7s	93·9s	22
and South-	Swingate (Dover)	90·0s	92·4s	94·4s	7
East	Wrotham	89·1s	91·3s	93·5s	120
South	Rowridge	88·5s	90·7s	92·9	60
	*Brighton	90·1s	92·3s	94·5s	0·15
	*Ventnor	89·4s	91·6s	93·8	0·02
West	Wenvoe	89·95s	96·8s	92·125s	120
	*Bath	88·8s	91·0s	93·2s	0·035
South-	Les Platons	91·1	94·75	97·1	1·5
West	North Hessary Tor	88·1	90·3s	92·5	60
	*Barnstaple	88·5s	90·7s	92·9s	0·15
	*Okehampton	88·7	90·9s	93·1	0·015
	Redruth	89·7	91·9s	94·1	9
	*Isles of Scilly	88·8	91·0s	93·2	0·02
Midlands	Sutton Coldfield	88·3s	90·5s	92·7s	120
	*Churchdown Hill	89·0s	91·2s	93·4s	0·025
	*Hereford	89·7s	91·9s	94·1s	0·025
	*Northampton	88·9s	91·1s	93·3s	0·06
East	Peterborough	90·1	92·3	94·5	20
	*Cambridge	88·9	91·1	93·3	0·02
	Tacolneston	89·7s	91·9s	94·1	120
North	Belmont	88·8s	90·9s	93·1s	8
	Holme Moss	89·3s	91·5s	93·7s	120
	*Scarborough	89·9s	92·1s	94·3s	0·025
	*Sheffield	89·9s	92·1s	94·3s	0·06
	*Wensleydale	88·3s	90·5s	92·7s	0·025
North-	Holme Moss	89·3s	91·5s	93·7s	120
West	*Douglas (IOM)	88·4	90·6	92·8	6
	*Kendal	88·7s	90·9s	93·1s	0·025
	*Morecambe Bay	90·0s	92·2s	94·4s	4
	*Windermere	88·6s	90·8s	93·0s	0·02
North-East	Pontop Pike	88·5s	90·7s	92·9s	60
	*Weardale	89·7s	91·9s	94·1s	0·1
	*Whitby	89·6s	91·8s	94·0s	0·04
	Sandale	88·1s	90·3s	94·7s	120
Northern	Divis	90·1s	92·3s	94·5s	60
Ireland	*Ballycastle	89·0	91·2	93·4	0·04
	*Brougher Mountain	88·9	91·1	93·3	2·5
	*Kilkeel	88·8	91·0	93·2	0·025
	*Larne	89·1	91·3	93·5	0·015
	*Londonderry	88·3	90·55	92·7	13
	*Maddybenny More	88·9	90·9	93·1	0·03
	*Newry	88·6	90·8	93·0	0·03
Scotland	Kirk o'Shotts	89·9s	92·1s	94·3s	120
(Radio	*Ashkirk	89·1s	91·3s	93·5s	18
Scotland)	*Ayr	88·7s	90·9s	93·1	0·055
	*Campbeltown	88·6s	90·8s	93·0s	0·035
	*Forfar	88·3s	90·5s	92·7s	10
	*Lochgilphead	88·3s	90·5s	92·7s	0·01
	*Millburn Muir	88·8s	91·0s	93·2s	0·025
	*Perth	89·0	91·2	93·4	0·015
	*Pitlochry	89·2	91·4	93·6	0·2
	*Rosneath	89·2s	91·4s	93·6s	0·025
	*Toward	88·5s	90·7s	92·9s	0·25
	*Meldrum	88·7	90·9	93·1	60

B.B.C. V.H.F./F.M. RADIO STATIONS

Service	Station	Radio 1/2	Radio 3 4	Radio	Max. erp kW
	*Bressay	88·3	90·5	92·7	10
	*Grantown	89·8	92·0	94·2	0·35
	*Kingussie	89·1	91·3	93·5	0·035
	*Orkney	89·3	91·5	93·7	20
	*Thrumster	90·1	92·3	94·5	10
	Rosemarkie	89·6	91·8	94·0	12
	*Ballachulish	88·1	90·3	92·5	0·015
	*Fort William	89·3	91·5	93·7	1·5
	*Kinlochleven	89·7	91·9	94·1	0·002
	*Melvaig	89·1	91·3	93·5	22
	*Oban	88·9	91·1	93·3	1·5
	*Penifiler	89·5	91·7	93·9	0·006
	*Skriaig	88·5	90·7	92·9	10
	Sandale	88·1s	90·3s	92·5s	120
Wales	Blaenplwyt	88·7	90·9	93·1	60
(Radio	*Dolgellau	90·1	92·3	94·5	0·015
Cymru)	*Ffestiniog	88·1	90·3	92·5	0·05
	*Machynlleth	89·4	91·6	93·8	0·06
	Haverfordwest	89·3	91·5	93·7	10
	Llanddona	89·6	91·8	94·0	12
	*Betws-y-Coed	88·2	90·4	92·6	0·01
	*Llangolien	88·85	91·05	93·25	10
	Wenvoe	89·95s	96·8s	94·3s	120
	*Brecon	88·9s	91·1s	93·3	0·01
	*Carmarthen	88·5s	90·7s	92·9s	0·01
	*Llandrindod Wells	89·1s	91·3s	93·5s	1·5
	*Llanidloes	88·1s	90·3s	92·5s	0·005

Frequencies in MHz, horizontal polarisation.
* Relay station.
s Transmits stereophonic programmes.

B.B.C. LOCAL RADIO STATIONS

	Medium wave kHz	m	kW	V.H.F. MHz	kW	Polarisation
Birmingham	1457	206	10	95·6	5·5	H
Blackburn	854	351	0·5	96·4	1·5	S
Brighton	1484	202	1	95·3	0·5	H
Bristol	1546	194	5	95·5	5	H
Carlisle (m.)	755	397	1	95·6	5	H
(r.)	1457	206	0·5	—	—	—
Cleveland	1546	194	1	96·6	5	H
Derby (m.)	1115	269	0·5	96·5	5·5	S
(r.)	—	—	—	94·2	0·01	V
Humberside	1484	202	2	96·9	4·5	H
Leeds	1106	271	1	92·4	5	S
Leicester	1594	188	0·5	95·1	0·3	S
London	1457	206	50	94·9	16·5	H
Manchester	1457	206	5	95·1	4	S
Medway	1034	290	0·5	96·7	5·5	H
Merseyside	1484	202	2	95·8	7·5	S
Newcastle	1457	206	2	95·4	3·5	H
Nottingham	1520	197	0·25	95·4	0·3	S
Oxford	1484	202	0·5	95·2	4·5	H

Sheffield (m.)	1034	290	1	97·4	5·2	S
(r.)	—	—	—	88·6	0·03	H
Solent (m.)	998	301	1	96·1	5	H
(r.)	1594	188	0·25	—	—	H
Stoke-on-Trent	1502	200	1	96·1	2·5	H

(m.)—main; (r.)—relay.

INDEPENDENT LOCAL RADIO STATIONS

| | Medium wave | | | | V.H.F. | |
	kHz	m	kW	MHz	kW	Polar-isation
Belfast						
Downtown Rad.	1025	293	1	96·0	1	C
Birmingham						
BRMB Radio	1151	261	0·8	94·8	1	C
Bradford						
Pennine Radio	1277	235	0·1	96·0	0·5	C
Edinburgh						
Radio Forth	1546	194	2*	96·8	0·5	C
Glasgow						
Radio Clyde	1151	261	2	95·1	3·4	C
Ipswich						
Radio Orwell	1169	257	0·3*	97·1	1	C
Liverpool						
Radio City	1546	194	1·2	96·7	5	C
London—General & Entertainment						
Capital Radio	1546	194	27·5	95·8	2	C
London—News & Information						
LBC	1151	261	5·5	97·3	2	C
Manchester						
Piccadilly Radio	1151	261	0·35	97·0	2	C
Nottingham						
Radio Trent	998	301	0·2	96·2	0·3	S
Plymouth						
Plymouth Sound	1151	261	0·5*	96·0	1	C
Portsmouth						
Radio Victory	1169	257	0·2*	95·0	0·2	C
Reading						
Thames Valley Broadcasting	1430	210	0·1*	97·0	0·5	C
Sheffield & Rotherham						
Radio Hallam	1546	194	0·3	95·2	0·1	H
				95·9	0·05	C
Swansea						
Swansea Sound	1169	257	0·8*	95·1	1	C
Teesside						
Radio Tees	1169	257	0·5*	95·0	2	C
Tyne/Wear						
Metro Radio	1151	261	1	97·0	5	C
Wolverhampton/ Black Country						
Beacon Radio	989	303	0·1*	97·2	1	C

Polarisation: H—horizontal; S—slant; V—vertical; C—circular.

B.B.C. V.H.F. TEST TONE TRANSMISSIONS

Transmission starts about 4 minutes after the end of Radio 3 programmes on Mondays and Saturdays.

Time min.	Left channel	Right channel	Purpose
—	250 Hz at zero level	440 Hz at zero level	Identification of left and right channels and setting of reference level
2	900 Hz at + 7 dB	900 Hz at + 7 dB, antiphase to left channel	Adjustment of phase of regenerated sub-carrier (see Note 4) and check of distortion with L-R signal only
6	900 Hz at + 7 dB	900 Hz + 7 dB, in phase with left channel	Check of distortion with L + R signal only
7	900 Hz at + 7 dB	No modulation	Check of L to R cross-talk
8	No modulation	900 Hz at + 7 dB	Check of R to L cross-talk
9	Tone sequence at − 4 dB: 60 Hz 900 Hz 5 kHz 10kHz This sequence is repeated	No modulation	Check of L-channel amplitude response and L to R cross-talk at high and low frequencies

Time min.	Left channel	Right channel	Purpose
≈ 11	No modulation	No modulation	Check of noise level in the presence of pilot
≈ 10	No modulation	Tone sequences as for left channel	Check of R-channel amplitude response and essential R to L cross-talk at high and low frequencies
T + 13	No modulation	Reversion to monophonic transmission	

Notes

1. This schedule is subject to variation or cancellation to accord with programme requirements and essential transmission tests.
2. The zero level reference corresponds to 40% of the maximum level of modulation applied to either stereophonic channel before pre-emphasis. All tests are transmitted momentarily at one-minute intervals.
3. Periods of tone lasting several minutes are interrupted with pre-emphasis.
4. With receivers having separate controls of subcarrier phase and crosstalk, the correct order of alignment is to adjust first the subcarrier phase to produce maximum output from either the L or the R channel and then to adjust the crosstalk (or 'separation') control for minimum crosstalk between channels.
5. With receivers in which the only control of crosstalk is by adjustment of subcarrier phase, this adjustment should be made on the crosstalk checks.
6. Adjustment of the balance control to produce equal loudness from the L and R loudspeakers is best carried out when listening to the announcements during a stereophonic transmission, which are made from a centre-stage position. Unless this adjustment is attempted during the transmission, the results may be confused because of the occurrence of standing-wave patterns in the listening room.
7. The outputs of most receivers include significant levels of the 19-kHz tone and its harmonics, which may affect signal-level meters. It is important, therefore, to provide filters with adequate loss at these frequencies if instruments are to be used for the above tests.

117

WAVELENGTH-FREQUENCY CONVERSION TABLE

Metres to Kilohertz

Metres	kHz	Metres	kHz
5	60,000	370	810·8
6	50,000	380	789·5
7	42,857	390	769·2
8	37,500	400	750
9	33,333	410	731·7
10	30,000	420	714·3
25	12,000	430	697·7
50	6,000	440	681·8
100	3,000	450	666·7
150	2,000	460	652·2
200	1,500	470	638·3
205	1,463	480	625
210	1,429	490	612·2
215	1,395	500	600
220	1,364	510	588·2
225	1,333	520	576·9
230	1,304	530	566
235	1,277	540	555·6
240	1,250	550	545·4
245	1,225	560	535·7
250	1,200	570	526·3
255	1,177	580	517·2
260	1,154	590	508·5
265	1,132	600	500
270	1,111	650	461·5
275	1,091	700	428·6
280	1,071	750	400
290	1,034	800	375
295	1,017	850	352·9
300	1,000	900	333·3
310	967·7	950	315·9
320	937·5	1,000	300
330	909·1	1,250	240
340	882·3	1,500	200
350	857·1	1,750	171·4
360	833·3	2,000	150

Note.—To convert kilohertz to wavelengths in metres, divide 300,000 by kilohertz.

To convert wavelengths in metres to kilohertz, divide 300,000 by the number of metres. One megahertz = 1,000,000 hertz or = 1,000 kilohertz. Thus, 30,000 kilohertz = 30 megahertz.

WORLD TIME

DIFFERENCE BETWEEN LOCAL TIME AND
GREENWICH MEAN TIME

The differences marked + indicate the number of hours ahead the GMT Differences marked − indicate the number of hours behind GMT

	Normal Time	Summer Time		Normal Time	Summer Time
Afars and Issas	+3	+3	Cambodia	+7	+7
Afghanistan	+4½	+4½	Cameroon	+1	+1
Alaska			Canada		
Juneau	−8	−8	(a) Newfndlnd.	−3½	−2½
General	−10	−10	(b) Atlantic	−4	−3
Nome and			(c) Eastern	−5	−4
Aleutians	−11	−11	(d) Central	−6	−5
Albania	+1	+1	(Alberta)	−7	−6
Algeria	GMT	GMT	(e) Pacific	−8	−7
Andorra	+1	+1	(f) Yukon	−9	−8
Angola	+1	+1	Canary Isl.	GMT	GMT
Argentina	−4	−3	Cape Verde Isl.	−2	−2
Ascension Isl.	GMT	GMT	Central African		
Australia			Rep.	+1	+1
(a) Victoria			Chad	+1	+1
New South			Chile	−4	−4
Wales,			China		
Queensland	+10	+10	General	+8	+8
Tasmania	+10	+11	Tibet and		
(b) N. Territory,			Urumchi	+6	+6
S. Australia	+9½	+9½	Colombia	−5	−5
(c) W. Australia	+8	+8	Comoro Isl.	+3	+3
Austria	+1	+1	Congo		
Azores	−1	−1	(Brazzaville)	+1	+1
			Costa Rica	−6	−6
			Cuba	−5	−5
Bahamas	−5	−5	Cyprus	+2	+2
Bahrain	+4	+4	Czechoslovakia	+1	+1
Bangladesh	+6	+6			
Barbados	−4	−4			
Belgium	+1	+1			
Bermuda	−4	−4			
Bolivia	−4	−4			
Botswana	+2	+2	Dahomey	+1	+1
Brazil			Denmark	+1	+1
(a) Eastern and			Dom. Rep.	−5	−4
Coastal	−3	−2			
(b) Manaos	−4	−3			
(c) Acre	−5	−4			
Brunei	+8	+8	Ecuador	−5	−5
Bulgaria	+2	+2	Egypt	+2	+3
Burma	+6½	+6½	El Salvador	−6	−6
Burundi	+2	+2	Ethiopia	+3	+3

	Normal Time	Summer Time		Normal Time	Summer Time
Falkland Isl.	-4	-3	Kenya	+3	+3
Faeroe Isl.	GMT	GMT	Korea	+9	+9
Fiji Islands	+12	+12	Kuwait	+3	+3
Finland	+2	+2			
France	+1	+1			
			Laos	+7	+7
			Lebanon	+2	+2
Gabon	+1	+1	Leeward Isl.	-4	-4
Gambia	GMT	GMT	Lesotho	+2	+2
Germany	+1	+1	Liberia	-¾	-¾
Ghana	GMT	GMT	Luxembourg	+1	+1
Gibraltar	+1	+1	Libya	+2	+2
Gilbert Isl.	+12	+12			
Great Britain	GMT	+1			
Greece	+2	+2	Macao	+8	+8
Greenland	-3	-3	Madagascar	+3	+3
Guadeloupe	-4	-4	Madeira	GMT	GMT
Guam	+10	+10	Malawi	+2	+2
Guatemala	-6	-6	Malaysia	+7½	+7½
Guiana	-3½	-3½	Maldive Isl.	+5½	+5½
Guiana (French)	-3	-3	Mali	GMT	GMT
Guinea	GMT	GMT	Mauritania	GMT	GMT
Guinea Equat.	+1	+1	Malta	+1	+1
Guinea Bissau	-1	-1	Marshall Isl.	+12	+12
			Martinique	-4	-4
Haiti	-5	-5	Mauritius	+4	+4
Hawaii	-10	-10	Mexico		
Holland	+1	+1	Generally	-6	-6
Honduras	-5	-6	Mongolia	+8	+9
Honduras (Belize)	-6	-5½	Morocco	GMT	GMT
Hong Kong	+8	+9	Mozambique	+2	+2
Hungary	+1	+1			
			Nauru	+11½	+11½
Iceland	-1	GMT	Nepal	+5·40	+5·40
India	+5½	+5½	Neth. Antilles	-4	-4
Indonesia			New Caledonia	+11	+11
(a) Java, Sumatra	+7	+7	New Guinea	+10	+10
(b) Borneo, Celebes, Bali	+8	+8	New Hebrides	+11	+11
(c) Moluccas, W. Irian	+9	+9	New Zealand	+12	+12
Iran	+3½	+3½	Nicaragua	-6	-6
Iraq	+3	+3	Niger	+1	+1
Ireland	+1	+1	Nigeria	+1	+1
Israel	+2	+2	Norway	+1	+1
Italy	+1	+1			
Ivory Coast	GMT	GMT	Oman	+4	+4
Jamaica	-5	-5	Pakistan	+5	+5
Japan	+9	+9	Panama	-5	-5
Jordan	+2	+2	Papua	+10	+10
			Paraguay	-4	-4
			Peru	-5	-5

	Normal Time	Summer Time		Normal Time	Summer Time
Philippines	+8	+8	Togo	GMT	GMT
Poland	+1	+1	Tonga Islands	+13	+13
Portugal	+1	+1	Trinidad	−4	−4
			Trucial States	+4	+4
Qatar	+4	+4	Tunisia	+1	+1
			Turkey	+2	+2
Reunion	+4	+4	Uganda	+3	+3
Rhodesia	+2	+2	Upper Volta	GMT	GMT
Rumania	+2	+2	Uruguay	−3	−3
Rwanda	+2	+2	U.S.A.		
			(a) Eastern Zone	−5	−4
Sabah	+8	+8	(b) Central Zone	−6	−5
Samoa Isl.	−11	−11	(c) Mountain Zone	−7	−6
St. Pierro	−3	−3	(d) Pacific Zone	−8	−7
S. Tomé	GMT	GMT	U.S.S.R.		
Sarawak	+8	+8	Moscow		
Saudi Arabia	+3	+3	Leningrad	+3	+3
Senegal	GMT	GMT	Baku	+4	+4
Seychelles	+4	+4	Sverdlovsk	+5	+5
Sierra Leone	GMT	GMT	Tashkent	+6	+6
Singapore	+7½	+7½	Novosibirsk	+7	+7
Solomon Isl.	+11	+11	Irkutsk	+8	+8
Somalia	+3	+3	Yakutsk	+9	+9
So. Africa	+2	+2	Khabarovsk	+10	+10
So. Yemen	+3	+3	Magadan	+11	+11
Spain	+1	+1	Petropavlovsk	+12	+12
Sri Lanka	+5½	+5½	Anadyr	+13	+13
Sudan	+2	+2			
Surinam	−3½	−3½	Venezuela	−4	−4
Swaziland	+2	+2	Vietnam	+7	+7
Sweden	+1	+1	Virgin Isl.	−4	−4
Switzerland	+1	+1			
Syria	+2	+3	Windward Isl.	−4	−4
			Yemen	+3	+3
Tahiti	−10	−10	Yugoslavia	+1	+1
Taiwan	+8	+9			
Tanzania	+3	+3	Zaire		
Tasmania	+10	+11	Kinshasa	+1	+1
Thailand	+7	+7	Lumumbashi	+2	+2
Timor	+8	+8	Zambia	+2	+2

INTERNATIONAL ALLOCATION OF CALL SIGNS

The first character or the first two characters of a call sign indicate the nationality of the station using it. In this list the abbreviation O.T. is used for overseas territories or states administered by, or for which the international relations are the responsibility of, the country named.

AAA–ALZ	U.S.A.	HUA–HUZ	Salvador
AMA–AOZ	Spain	HVA–HVZ	Vatican State
APA–ASZ	Pakistan	HWA–HYZ	France and O.T.
ATA–AWZ	India	HZA–HZZ	Saudi Arabia
AXA–AXZ	Australia	IAA–IZZ	Italy and O.T.
AYA–AZZ	Argentina	JAA–JSZ	Japan
BAA–BZZ	China	JTA–JVZ	Mongolia
CAA–CEZ	Chile	JWA–JXZ	Norway
CFA–CKZ	Canada	JYA–JYZ	Jordan
CLA–CMZ	Cuba	JZA–JZZ	Neth. New
CNA–CNZ	Morocco	KAA–KZZ	U.S.A. (Guinea
COA–COZ	Cuba	LAA–LNZ	Norway
CPA–CPZ	Bolivia	LOA–LWZ	Argentina
CQA–CRZ	Portuguese O.T.	LXA–LXZ	Luxembourg
CSA–CUZ	Portugal	LYA–LYZ	Lithuania
CVA–CXZ	Uruguay	LZA–LZZ	Bulgaria
CYA–CZZ	Canada	MAA–MZZ	U.K.
DAA–DTZ	Germany	NAA–NZZ	U.S.A.
DUA–DZZ	Philippines	OAA–OCZ	Peru
EAA–EHZ	Spain	ODA–ODZ	Lebanon
EIA–EJZ	Eire	OEA–OEZ	Austria
EKA–EKZ	U.S.S.R.	OFA–OJZ	Finland
ELA–ELZ	Liberia	OKA–OMZ	Czechoslovakia
EMA–EOZ	U.S.S.R.	ONA–OTZ	Belgium
EPA–EQZ	Iran	OUA–OZZ	Denmark
ERA–ERZ	U.S.S.R.	PAA–PIZ	Netherlands
ESA–ESZ	Estonia	PJA–PJZ	Netherlands An-
ETA–ETZ	Ethiopia	PKA–POZ	Indonesia (tilles
EUA–EWZ	Byelorussia	PPA–PYZ	Brazil
EXA–EZZ	U.S.S.R.	PZA–PZZ	Surinam
FAA–FZZ	France and O.T.	QAA–QZZ	(Q Code)
GAA–GZZ	U.K.	RAA–RZZ	U.S.S.R.
HAA–HAZ	Hungary	SAA–SMZ	Sweden
HBA–HBZ	Switzerland	SNA–SRZ	Poland
HCA–HDZ	Ecuador	SSA–SSM	Egypt
HEA–HEZ	Switzerland	SSN–STZ	Sudan
HFA–HFZ	Poland	SUA–SUZ	Egypt
HGA–HGZ	Hungary	SVA–SZZ	Greece
HHA–HHZ	Haiti	TAA–TCZ	Turkey
HIA–HIZ	Dominican Republic	TDA–TDZ	Guatemala
HJA–HKZ	Colombia	TEA–TEZ	Costa Rica
HLA–HMZ	Korea	TFA–TFZ	Iceland
HNA–HNZ	Iraq	TGA–TGZ	Guatemala
HOA–HPZ	Panama	THA–THZ	France and O.T.
HQA–HRZ	Honduras Republic	TIA–TIZ	Costa Rica
HSA–HSZ	Thailand	TJA–TRZ	France and O.T.
HTA–HTZ	Nicaragua	TSA–TSM	Tunisia

TSN–TZZ	France and O.T.	4DA–4IZ	Philippines
UAA–UQZ	U.S.S.R.	4JA–4LZ	U.S.S.R.
URA–UTZ	Ukraine	4MA–4MZ	Venezuela
UUA–UZZ	U.S.S.R.	4NA–4OZ	Yugoslavia
VAA–VGZ	Canada	4PA–4SZ	Ceylon
VHA–VNZ	Australia	4TA–4TZ	Peru
VOA–VOZ	Canada	4UA–4UZ	United Nations
VPA–VSZ	U.K. Overseas Ter.	4VA–4VZ	Haiti
VTA–VWZ	India	4WA–4WZ	Yemen
VXA–VYZ	Canada	4XA–4XZ	Israel
VZA–VZZ	Australia	4YA–4YZ	International Civil
WAA–WZZ	U.S.A.		Aviation Organiz-
XAA–XIZ	Mexico	4ZA–4ZZ	Israel ation
XJA–XOZ	Canada	5AA–5AZ	Libya
XPA–XPZ	Denmark	5CA–5GZ	Morocco
XQA–XRZ	Chile	5HA–5IZ	Tanganyika
XSA–XSZ	China	5JA–5KZ	Colombia
XTA–XTZ	France and O.T.	5LA–5MZ	Liberia
XUA–XUZ	Cambodia	5NA–5OZ	Nigeria
XVA–XVZ	Vietnam	5PA–5QZ	Denmark
XWA–XWZ	Laos	5RA–5VZ	France and O.T.
XXA–XXZ	Portuguese O.T.	5WA–5WZ	W. Samoa
XYA–XZZ	Burma	5YA–5ZZ	Kenya
YAA–YAZ	Afghanistan	6AA–6BZ	Egypt
YBA–YHZ	Indonesia	6CA–6CZ	Syria
YIA–YIZ	Iraq	6DA–6JZ	Mexico
YJA–YJZ	New Hebrides	6KA–6NZ	Korea
YKA–YKZ	Syria	6OA–6OZ	Somali
YLA–YLZ	Latvia	6PA–6SZ	Pakistan
YMA–YMZ	Turkey	6TA–6UZ	Sudan
YNA–YNZ	Nicaragua	6XA–6XZ	Malagasy
YOA–YRZ	Rumania	6YA–6YZ	Jamaica
YSA–YSZ	Salvador	7AA–7IZ	Indonesia
YTA–YUZ	Yugoslavia	7JA–7NZ	Japan
YVA–YYZ	Venezuela	7RA–7RZ	Algeria
YZA–YZZ	Yugoslavia	7SA–7SZ	Sweden
ZAA–ZAZ	Albania	7TA–7YZ	Algeria
ZBA–ZJZ	U.K. Overseas Ter.	7ZA–7ZZ	Saudi Arabia
ZKA–ZMZ	New Zealand	8AA–8IZ	Indonesia
ZNA–ZOZ	U.K. Overseas Ter.	8JA–8NZ	Japan
ZPA–ZPZ	Paraguay	8SA–8SZ	Sweden
ZQA–ZQZ	U.K. Overseas Ter.	8TA–8YZ	India
ZRA–ZUZ	South Africa	8ZA–8ZZ	Saudi Arabia
ZVA–ZZZ	Brazil	9AA–9AZ	San Marino
2AA–2ZZ	U.K.	9BA–9DZ	Iran
3AA–3AZ	Monaco	9EA–9FZ	Ethiopia
3BA–3FZ	Canada	9GA–9GZ	Ghana
3GA–3GZ	Chile	9KA–9KZ	Kuwait
3HA–3UZ	China	9LA–9LZ	Sierra Leone
3VA–3VZ	Tunisia	9MA–9MZ	Malaysia
3WA–3WZ	Vietnam	9NA–9NZ	Nepal
3YA–3YZ	Norway	9OA–9UZ	Congo
3XA–3XZ	Guinea	9UA–9UZ	Burundi
3ZA–3ZZ	Poland	9VA–9WZ	Malaysia
4AA–4CZ	Mexico	9XA–9XZ	Rwanda

AMATEUR BANDS IN THE U.K.
Amateur (Sound) and (Sound Mobile) Licences

Frequency bands (MHz)	Maximum d.c. input power
1·8–2	10 W
3·5–3·8 7–7·10 14–14·35 21–21·45 28–29·7	150 W
70·025–70·7	50 W
144–145 145–146 430–440 1,215–1,325 2,300–2,450 3,400–3,475 5,650–5,850 10,000–10,500 21,000–22,000	150 W
2,350–2,400 5,700–5,800 10,050–10,450 21,150–21,850	25 W mean power and 2·5 kW peak power

There are certain restrictions on the type of broadcast and class of emission on all frequency bands. A detailed list is available from the Ministry of Posts and Tele-communications.

DIPOLE LENGTHS FOR THE AMATEUR BANDS

Amateur Band (metres)	Dipole Length (metres)
80	39
40	20·2
20	10·1
15	6·7
10	5·0

MICROWAVE BAND DESIGNATION SYSTEMS

M.O.D. discontinued system		New N.A.T.O. designation system	
	GHz		GHz
P	0·08–0·39	A	0–0·25
L₂	0·39–1·0	B	0·25–0·5
L₁	1·0–2·5	C	0·5–1·0
S	2·5–4·1	D	1·0–2
C	4·1–7·0	E	2–3
X	7·0–11·5	F	3–4
J	11·5–18·0	G	4–6
K	18–33	H	6–8
Q	33–40	I	8–10
O	40–60	J	10–20
V	60–90	K	20–40
		L	40–60
		M	60–100

U.K. I.E.E. recommended system		U.S.A system	
	GHz		GHz
L	1–2	P	0·225–0·39
S	2–4	L	0·39–1·55
C	4–8	S	1·55–5·2
X	7–12	X	5·2–10·9
J	12–18	K	10·9–36
K	18–26	Q	36–46
Q	26–40	V	45–56
V	40–60	W	56–100
O	30–90		

INTERNATIONAL 'Q' CODE

Abbrev.	Question	Answer for Advice
QRA	What is the name of your station?	The name of my station is ...
QRB	How far approximately are you from my station?	The approximate distance is ... miles
QRD	Where are you bound and where are you from?	I am bound for ... from ...
QRG	Will you tell me my exact frequency in kHz?	Your exact frequency is ... kHz.
QRH	Does my frequency vary?	Your frequency varies.
QRI	Is my note good?	Your note varies.
QRJ	Do you receive me badly?	I cannot receive you.
	Are my signals weak?	Your signals are too weak.
QRK	Do you receive me well? Are my signals good?	I receive you well. Your signals are good.
QRL	Are you busy?	I am busy. Please do not interfere.
QRM	Are you being interfered with?	I am being interfered with.
QRN	Are you troubled by atmospherics?	I am troubled by atmospherics.
QRO	Shall I increase power?	Increase power.
QRP	Shall I decrease power?	Decrease power.
QRQ	Shall I send faster?	Send faster (... words per minute).
QRS	Shall I send more slowly?	Send more slowly (... words per minute).
QRT	Shall I stop sending?	Stop sending.
QRU	Have you anything for me?	I have nothing for you

INTERNATIONAL 'Q' CODE

Abbrev.	Question	Answer for Advice
QRV	Are you ready?	I am ready.
QRX	Shall I wait? When will you call me again?	Wait (or wait until I have finished communicating with . . .) I will call you at . . . GMT.
QRZ	Who is calling me?	You are being called by . . .
QSA	What is the strength of my signals? (1 to 5)	The strength of your signals is . . . (1 to 5).
QSB	Does the strength of my signals vary?	The strength of your signals varies.
QSD	Is my keying correct? Are my signals distinct?	Your keying is indistinct. Your signals are bad.
QSL	Can you give me acknowledgement of receipt?	I give you acknowledgment of receipt.
QSM	Shall I repeat the last telegram (message) I sent you?	Repeat the last telegram (message) you have sent me.
QSO	Can you communicate with . . . direct (or through the medium of . . .)?	I can communicate with . . . direct (or through the medium of . . .).
QSP	Will you relay to . . .?	I will relay to . . .
QSV	Shall I send a series of V's?	Send a series of V's.
QSX	Will you listen for . . . (call sign) on . . . kHz?	I am listening for . . . (call sign) on . . . kHz.
QSZ	Shall I send each word or group twice?	Send each word or group twice.
QTH	What is your position in latitude and longitude?	My position is . . . latitude . . . longitude.
QTR	What is the exact time?	The exact time is . . .

127

MISCELLANEOUS INTERNATIONAL ABBREVIATIONS

Abbrev.	Meaning	Abbrev.	Meaning
C	Yes	GA	Resume sending
N	No	MN	Minute/minutes
W	Word	NW	I resume transmission
AA	All after ...	OK	Agreed
AB	All before ...	UA	Are we agreed?
AL	All that has just been sent	WA	Word after ...
		WB	Word before ...
BN	All between	XS	Atmospherics
CL	I am closing my station		

AMATEUR ABBREVIATIONS

Abbrev.	Meaning	Abbrev.	Meaning
ABT	About	NIL	Nothing
AGN	Again	NM	No more
ANI	Any	NR	Number
BA	Buffer amplifier	NW	Now
BCL	Broadcast listener	OB	Old boy
BD	Bad	OM	Old Man
BI	By	OT	Old timer
BK	Break in	PA	Power amplifier
BN	Been	PSE	Please
CK	Check	R	Received all sent
CKT	Circuit	RAC	Rectified A.C.
CLD	Called	RCD	Received
CO	Crystal oscillator	RX	Receiver
CUD	Could	SA	Say
CUL	See you later	SED	Said
DX	Long distance	SIGS	Signals
ECO	Electron-coupled oscillator	SIGN	Signature
		SSS	Single signal super-heterodyne
ES	And		
FB	Fine business (good work)	SKD	Schedule
		TKS	Thanks
FD	Frequency doubler	TMN	To-morrow
FM	From	TNX	Thanks
GA	Go ahead, or Good afternoon	TPTG	Tuned plate tuned grid
		TX	Transmitter
GB	Good-bye	U	You
GE	Good evening	UR	You are
GM	Good morning	VY	Very
GN	Good night	WDS	Words
HAM	Radio amateur	WKG	Working
HI	Laughter	WL	Will
HR	Hear, or here	WUD	Would
HRD	Heard	WX	Weather
HV	Have	YF	Wife
LTR	Later	YL	Young lady
MILS	Milliamperes	YR	Your
MO	Meter oscillator	73	Kind regards
ND	Nothing doing	88	Love and kisses

QSA CODE (Signal Strength)

QSA1	.	Hardly perceptible; unreadable.
QSA2	.	Weak, readable now and then.
QSA3	.	Fairly good; readable, but with difficulty.
QSA4	.	Good; readable.
QSA5	.	Very good; perfectly readable.

QRK CODE (Audibility)

R1	.	Unreadable.
R2	.	Weak signals; barely readable.
R3	.	Weak signals; but can be copied.
R4	.	Fair signals; easily readable.
R5	.	Moderately strong signals.
R6	.	Good signals.
R7	.	Good strong signals.
R8	.	Very strong signals.
R9	.	Extremely strong signals.

RST CODE (Readability)

1	.	Unreadable.
2	.	Barely readable, occasional words distinguishable.
3	.	Readable with considerable difficulty.
4	.	Readable with practically no difficulty.
5	.	Perfectly readable.

(Signal Strength)

1	.	Faint, signals barely perceptible.
2	.	Very weak signals.
3	.	Weak signals.
4	.	Fair signals.
5	.	Fairly good signals.
6	.	Good signals.
7	.	Moderately strong signals.
8	.	Strong signals.
9	.	Extremely strong signals.

(Tone)

1	.	Extremely rough hissing note.
2	.	Very rough A.C. note, no trace of musicality.
3	.	Rough, low-pitched A.C. note, slightly musical.
4	.	Rather rough A.C. note, moderately musical.
5	.	Musically modulated note.
6	.	Modulated note, slight trace of whistle.
7	.	Near D.C. note, smooth ripple.
8	.	Good D.C. note, just a trace of ripple.
9	.	Purest D.C. note.

(If the note appears to be crystal-controlled add an X after the appropriate number.)

INTERNATIONAL MORSE CODE

A	dit dah	·—
B	dah dit dit dit	—···
C	dah dit dah dit	—·—·
D	dah dit dit	—··
E	dit	·
F	dit dit dah dit	··—·
G	dah dah dit	——·
H	dit dit dit dit	····
I	dit dit	··
J	dit dah dah dah	·———
K	dah dit dah	—·—
L	dit dah dit dit	·—··
M	dah dah	——
N	dah dit	—·
O	dah dah dah	———
P	dit dah dah dit	·——·
Q	dah dah dit dah	——·—
R	dit dah dit	·—·
S	dit dit dit	···
T	dah	—
U	dit dit dah	··—
V	dit dit dit dah	···—
W	dit dah dah	·——
X	dah dit dit dah	—··—
Y	dah dit dah dah	—·——
Z	dah dah dit dit	——··

Number Code

1	dit dah dah dah dah	·————
2	dit dit dah dah dah	··———
3	dit dit dit dah dah	···——
4	dit dit dit dit dah	····—
5	dit dit dit dit dit	·····
6	dah dit dit dit dit	—····
7	dah dah dit dit dit	——···
8	dah dah dah dit dit	———··
9	dah dah dah dah dit	————·
0	dah dah dah dah dah	—————

Note of interrogation	dit dit dah dah dit dit	··——··
Note of exclamation	dah dah dit dit dah dah	——··——
Apostrophe	dit dah dah dah dah dit	·————·
Hyphen	dah dit dit dit dit dah	—····—
Fractional bar	dah dit dit dah dit	—··—·
Brackets	dah dit dah dah dit dah	—·——·—
Inverted commas	dit dah dit dit dah dit	·—··—·
Underline	dit dit dah dah dit dah	··——·—
Prelim. call	dah dit dah dit dah	—·—·—
Break sign	dah dit dit dit dah	—···—
End message	dit dah dit dah dit	·—·—·
Error	dit dit dit dit dit dit	······

PHONETIC ALPHABET

To avoid the possibility of the letters of a call-sign being misunderstood, it is usual to use the words given below in place of the letters. For example, G6PY would be given as G6 Papa Yankee.

Letter	Code Word	Pronunciation
A	Alfa	*AL* FAH
B	Bravo	*BRAH* VOH
C	Charlie	*CHAR* LEE
D	Delta	*DELL* TAH
E	Echo	*ECK* OH
F	Foxtrot	*FOKS* TROT
G	Golf	GOLF
H	Hotel	HOH *TELL*
I	India	*IN* DEE AH
J	Juliett	*JEW* LEE *ETT*
K	Kilo	*KEY* LOH
L	Lima	*LEE* MAH
M	Mike	MIKE
N	November	NO *VEM* BER
O	Oscar	*OSS* CAH
P	Papa	PAH *PAH*
Q	Quebec	KEH *BECK*
R	Romeo	*ROW* ME OH
S	Sierra	SEE *AIR* RAH
T	Tango	*TANG* GO
U	Uniform	*YOU* NEE FORM
V	Victor	*VIK* TAH
W	Whiskey	*WISS* KEY
X	X-ray	*ECKS* RAY
Y	Yankee	*YANG* KEY
Z	Zulu	*ZOO* LOO

Syllables in italic carry the accent.

CHARACTERISTICS OF WORLD TELEVISION SYSTEMS

System	No. of lines	Channel width MHz	Vision Bandwidth MHz	Vision/Sound separation MHz	Vision modulation	Sound modulation	Field frequency
A	405	5	3	−3·5	POS.	A.M.	50
B	625	7	5	+5·5	NEG.	F.M.	50
C	625	7	5	+5·5	POS.	A.M.	50
D	625	8	6	+6·5	NEG.	F.M.	50
E	819	14	10	±11·15	POS.	A.M.	50
F	819	7	5	+5·5	POS.	F.M.	50
G	625	8	5·5	+5·5	NEG.	F.M.	50
I	625	8	5·5	+6	NEG.	F.M.	50
K	625	8	6	+6·5	NEG.	F.M.	50
L	625	8	6	+6·5	POS.	A.M.	50
M	525	6	4·2	+4·5	NEG.	F.M.	60
N	625	6	4·2	+4·5	NEG.	F.M.	50

A—U.K., Eire
B—Most of Western Europe, Australia, New Zealand
D—U.S.S.R. and Eastern Europe except East Germany
E—France, Monaco
I—Luxembourg
I—U.K. and Eire
K—French Overseas Territories
L—France 625 system
M—U.S.A., most of Central and South America, Japan and others

405-LINE TELEVISION CHANNELS

Channel No.		Sound (MHz)	Vision (MHz)
BAND I	1	41·50	45·00
	2	48·25	51·75
	3	53·25	56·75
	4	58·25	61·75
	5	63·25	66·75
BAND III	6	176·25	179·75
	7	181·25	184·75
	8	186·25	189·75
	9	191·25	194·75
	10	196·25	199·75
	11	201·25	204·75
	12	206·25	209·75
	13	211·25	214·75

625-LINE TELEVISION CHANNELS
BANDS IV AND V

Channel No.	Frequencies (MHz)	Channel No.	Frequencies (MHz)
21	470–478	45	662–670
22	478–486	46	670–678
23	486–494	47	678–686
24	494–502	48	686–694
25	502–510	49	694–702
26	510–518	50	702–710
27	518–526	51	710–718
28	526–534	52	718–726
29	534–542	53	726–734
30	542–550	54	734–742
31	550–558	55	742–750
32	558–566	56	750–758
33	566–574	57	758–766
34	574–582	58	766–774
35	582–590	59	774–782
36	590–598	60	782–790
37	598–606	61	790–798
38	606–614	62	798–806
39	614–622	63	806–814
40	622–630	64	814–822
41	630–638	65	822–830
42	638–646	66	830–838
43	646–654	67	838–846
44	654–662	68	846–854

U.H.F. TELEVISION CHANNEL GROUPS

Area	Channel Groups			
Belfast (Divis)	21	24	27	31
Caithness	21	24	27	31
Cardiganshire	21	24	27	31
East Lothian	21	24	27	31
Huntingdon	21	24	27	31
Isle of Wight (Rowridge)	21	24	27	31
West Yorks	21	24	27	31
Argyllshire	22	25	28	32
Cumberland	22	25	28	32
East Cornwall	22	25	28	32
East Lincs	22	25	28	32
Fermanagh	22	25	28	32
Herefordshire	22	25	28	32
Kincardine (Durris)	22	25	28	32
Ayrshire	23	26	29	33
Banff	23	26	29	33
East Devon	23	26	29	33
Lewis	23	26	29	33
London (Crystal Palace)	23	26	30	33
North Yorks	23	26	29	33
Staffordshire	23	26	29	33
Isle of Man	30	34	48	52
Shetland	32	34	45	49
Flintshire	39	42	45	49
Hampshire	39	42	45	66
Inverness	39	42	45	49
Northumberland	39	42	45	49
B'ham (Sutton Coldfield)	40	43	46	50
Dorset	40	43	46	50
Lanarkshire (Black Hill)	40	43	46	50
North Kent	40	43	46	65
North Lancs	40	43	46	56
Orkney	40	43	46	50
Pembrokeshire	40	43	46	50
Guildford	40	43	46	50
Tunbridge Wells	41	44	47	51
Buchan	41	44	47	51
Caernarvonshire	41	44	47	51
Jersey	41	44	47	51
Kirkcudbrightshire	41	44	47	51
Londonderry	41	44	47	51

Area	Channel Groups			
South Yorks (Emley Moor)	41	44	47	51
South Wales (Wenvoe)	41	44	47	51
Suffolk	41	44	47	51
West Cornwall	41	44	47	51
Guernsey	48	52	54	56
East Sussex	49	52	64	67
South-east Kent (Dover)	50	53	56	66
Anglesey (Llanddona)	53	57	60	63
Carmarthenshire	53	57	60	63
East Yorks	53	57	60	63
Northamptonshire	53	57	60	63
Perthshire	53	57	60	63
South Devon	53	57	60	63
Wigtown	53	57	60	63
Reigate	53	57	60	63
Hertford	54	58	61	64
Armagh	54	58	61	64
Bristol	54	58	61	64
Dumbarton	54	58	61	64
Durham (Pontop Pike)	54	58	61	64
Nottinghamshire	54	58	61	64
West Sussex	55	58	61	68
Norfolk (Tacolneston)	55	59	62	65
North Antrim	55	59	62	65
North Devon	55	59	62	65
Selkirkshire	55	59	62	65
South Lancs (Winter Hill)	55	59	62	65

AERIAL DIMENSIONS

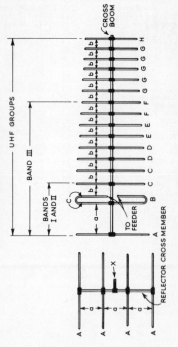

Pattern of general-purpose Yagi array to be used in conjunction with the dimensions given on p. 137.

AERIAL DIMENSIONS

Channel		A	B	C	D	E	F	G	H	a	b	c
					Dimensions in cm							
BAND I	1	341	325	299	—	—	—	—	—	171	102	3·8
	2	299	285	257	—	—	—	—	—	148	89	3·8
	3	272	257	235	—	—	—	—	—	135	82	3·8
	4	248	235	218	—	—	—	—	—	125	74	3·8
	5	230	218	200	—	—	—	—	—	115	69	3·8
BAND II		169	160	146	—	—	—	—	—	82	50·5	3·8
BAND III	6	84	80	75	73	72	71	—	—	44	21·5	2·5
	7	83	77	73	71	70	69	—	—	43	21	2·5
	8	82	74	70	68	65	64	—	—	41·5	20·5	2·5
	9	80	72	68	66	65	64	—	—	40	20	2·5
	10	75	71	66	64	62	62	—	—	39	19·5	2·5
	11	74	70	64	62	61	60	—	—	38	19	2·5
	12	73	69	62	61	60	59	—	—	37	18·5	2·5
	13	72	68	61	60	59	57	—	—	36	18	2·5
U.H.F. GROUPS	A	30·1	30	24·1	23	22·8	21·1	20·4	19·9	10·3	10·3	1·8
	B	26·5	21·7	18·9	18	17·8	16·5	15·5	15·5	8·9	8·9	1·8
	C	23·2	18·2	16	15·5	16·1	14	13·3	13·2	7·6	7·6	1·8
	D	26·1	23·5	18·4	15·3	15·5	14·8	13·8	13·2	7·5	7·5	1·8
	E	27	26·5	21·1	18·6	17·9	17·6	16	15·8	15·8	18	2·5

Channels covered in the u.h.f. groups are:

Group Letter	Colour Code	Channels
A	Red	21-34
B	Yellow	39-51
C	Green	50-66
D	Blue	49-68
E	Brown	39-68

137

EUROPEAN
V.H.F. SOUND BROADCASTING CHANNELS

Channel	MHz	Channel	MHz
2	87·6	30	96·0
3	87·9	31	96·3
4	88·2	32	96·6
5	88·5	33	96·9
6	88·8	34	97·2
7	89·1	35	97·5
8	89·4	36	97·8
9	89·7	37	98·1
10	90·0	38	98·4
11	90·3	39	98·7
12	90·6	40	99·0
13	90·9	41	99·3
14	91·2	42	99·6
15	91·5	43	99·9
16	91·8	44	100·2
17	92·1	45	100·5
18	92·4	46	100·8
19	92·7	47	101·1
20	93·0	48	101·4
21	93·3	49	101·7
22	93·6	50	102·0
23	93·9	51	102·3
24	94·2	52	102·6
25	94·5	53	102·9
26	94·8	54	103·2
27	95·1	55	103·5
28	95·4	56	103·8
29	95·7		

METRIC SYSTEM

List of Prefixes

mega   means a million times.
kilo   means a thousand times.
hecto means a hundred times.
deca   means ten times.
deci   means a tenth part of.
centi   means a hundredth part of.
milli   means a thousandth part of.
micro means a millionth part of.

Square Measure

100 sq. metres	= 1 are
10,000 sq. metres	= 1 hectare

Weight

10 grammes	= 1 decagramme
10 decagrammes	= 1 hectogramme
10 hectogrammes	= 1 kilogramme
1,000 kilogrammes	= 1 tonne

Capacity

1 litre	= 1 cubic decimetre
10 litres	= 1 decalitre
10 decalitres	= 1 hectolitre
10 hectolitres	= 1 kilolitre

Length

10 millimetres	= 1 centimetre
10 centimetres	= 1 decimetre
10 decimetres	= 1 metre
10 metres	= 1 decametre
10 decametres	= 1 hectometre
10 hectometres	= 1 kilometre
10 kilometres	= 1 myriametre

Linear Measure Equivalents

1 inch	= 2·54 centimetres, or 25·4 millimetres
1 foot	= 30·48 centimetres, 304·8 millimetres, or 0·3048 metre
1 yard	= 0·9144 metre
1 mile	= 1·6093 kilometres = 5,280 feet
1 millimetre	= 0·03937 inch
1 centimetre	= 0·3937 inch
1 decimetre	= 3·937 inches
1 metre	= 39·3701 inches
	3·28084 feet
	1·09361 yards
1 kilometre	= 0·62137 mile
1 decametre (10 metres)	= 10·936 yards

METRIC CONVERSION FACTORS

To convert—

Millimetres to inches	× 0·03937 or ÷ 25·4
Centimetres to inches	× 0·3937 or ÷ 2·54
Metres to inches	× 39·37
Metres to feet	× 3·281
Metres to yards	× 1·094
Metres per second to feet per minute	× 197
Kilometres to miles	× 0·6214 or ÷ 1·6093
Kilometres to feet	× 3,280·8693
Square millimetres to square inches	× 0·00155 or ÷ 645·1
Square centimetres to square inches	× 0·155 or ÷ 6·451
Square metres to square feet	× 10·764
Square metres to square yards	× 1·2

140

METRIC CONVERSION FACTORS
—continued

To convert—

Square kilometres to acres	× 247·1
Hectares to acres	× 2·471
Cubic centimetres to cubic inches	× 0·06 or ÷ 16·383
Cubic metres to cubic feet	× 35·315
Cubic metres to cubic yards	× 1·308
Litres to cubic inches	× 61·022
Litres to gallons	× 0·21998 or ÷ 4·545
Hectolitres to cubic feet	× 3·531
Hectolitres to cubic yards	× 0·131
Grammes to ounces (avoirdupois)	× 0·035 or ÷ 28·35
Grammes per cubic cm. to lb. per cubic inch	÷ 27·7
Joules to foot-lb.	× 0·7373
Kilogrammes to oz.	× 35·3
Kilogrammes to lb.	× 2·2046
Kilogrammes to tons	× 0·001
Kilogrammes per sq. cm. to lb. per square inch	× 14·223
Kilogramme-metres to foot-lb.	× 7·233
Kilogramme per metre to lb. per foot	× 0·672
Kilogramme per cubic metre to lb. per cubic foot	× 0·062
Kilogramme per cheva-vapeur to lb. per h.p.	× 2·235
Kilowatts to h.p.	× 134
Watts to h.p.	÷ 7·46
Watts to foot-lb. per second	× 0·7373
Cheval-vapeur to h.p.	× 0·9863
Gallons of water to lb.	× 10
Atmospheres to lb. per square inch	× 14·7

EQUIVALENTS OF IMPERIAL AND METRIC WEIGHTS AND MEASURES

IMPERIAL		METRIC
Linear Measure		
1 inch	25·4 millimetres	1 millimetre	0·03937 inch
1 foot	304·8 millimetres	1 centimetre	0·3937 inch
1 yard	0·9144 metre	**1 metre**	**39·370 inches**
1 chain (22 yards)	20·1168 metres	1 metre	3·28084 feet
1 furlong (220 yards)	201·168 metres	1 metre	1·09361 yards
1 mile (8 furlongs)	1·6093 kilometres	1 kilometre	0·62137 mile
Square Measure		
1 sq. inch	645·16 sq. mm	1 sq. cm	0·15500 sq. inch
1 sq. foot	0·0929 sq. metre	1 sq. metre	10·7639 sq. feet
1 sq. yard	0·836126 sq. metre	1 sq. metre	1·1960 sq. yards
1 rood (1,210 sq. yd)	10·117 ares	1 are (100 sq. m)	119·60 sq. yards
1 acre (4,840 sq. yd)	0·40468 hectare	1 hectare (100 ares)	2·4711 acres
1 sq. mile (640 acres)	259·00 hectares	1 sq. kilometre	0·38600 sq. miles

EQUIVALENTS OF IMPERIAL AND METRIC
WEIGHTS AND MEASURES—*cont.*

IMPERIAL		METRIC

Cubic Measure

IMPERIAL		METRIC
1 cu. inch	16·387 cu. cm	1 cu. cm	0·0610 cu. inch
1 cu. foot	0·028317 cu. m	1 cu. metre	35·3148 cu. feet
1 cu. yard	0·764553 cu. m	1 cu. metre	1·307954 cu. yards

Capacity Measure

IMPERIAL		METRIC
1 pint	0·568 litre	1 centilitre	0·070 gill
1 quart	1·136 litres	1 litre	1·75980 pints
1 gallon	4·546 litres	1 litre	0·2199 gallons

Weight

IMPERIAL		METRIC
1 grain	0·0648 gramme	1 milligramme	0·015 grain
1 dram	1·772 grammes	1 centigramme	0·154 grain
1 ounce	28·350 grammes	1 gramme	15·432 grains
1 pound	0·453592 kilogrammes	1 hectogramme	1·543 grains
1 stone	6·350 kilogrammes	1 kilogramme	2·20462 lb
1 quarter	12·70 kilogrammes	1 myriagramme	22·046 lb
1 cwt	50·80 kilogrammes	1 quintal (100 kg)	1·968 cwt
1 ton	1·0160 tonnes	1 tonne (1,000 kg)	0·9842 ton

Fractions of an inch	Decimals of an inch	mm	Fractions of an inch	Decimals of an inch	mm
1/64	0·0156	0·397	33/64	0·5156	13·097
1/32	0·0312	0·794	17/32	0·5313	13·494
3/64	0·0469	1·191	35/64	0·5469	13·891
1/16	0·0625	1·588	9/16	0·5625	14·287
5/64	0·0781	1·984	37/64	0·5781	14·684
3/32	0·0938	2·381	19/32	0·5938	15·081
7/64	0·1094	2·778	39/64	0·6094	15·478
1/8	0·1250	3·175	5/8	0·6250	15·875
9/64	0·1406	3·572	41/64	0·6406	16·272
5/32	0·1563	3·969	21/32	0·6563	16·668
11/64	0·1719	4·366	43/64	0·6719	17·065
3/16	0·1875	4·762	11/16	0·6875	17·462
13/64	0·2031	5·159	45/64	0·7031	17·859
7/32	0·2187	5·556	23/32	0·7188	18·256
15/64	0·2344	5·953	47/64	0·7344	18·653
1/4	0·2500	6·350	3/4	0·7500	19·050
17/64	0·2656	6·747	49/64	0·7656	19·447
9/32	0·2813	7·144	25/32	0·7813	19·843
19/64	0·2969	7·541	51/64	0·7969	20·240
5/16	0·3125	7·937	13/16	0·8125	20·637
21/64	0·3281	8·334	53/64	0·8281	21·034
11/32	0·3438	8·731	27/32	0·8438	21·431
23/64	0·3594	9·128	55/64	0·8594	21·828
3/8	0·3750	9·525	7/8	0·8750	22·225
25/64	0·3906	9·922	57/64	0·8906	22·622
13/32	0·4062	10·319	29/32	0·9062	23·019
27/64	0·4219	10·716	59/64	0·9219	23·416
7/16	0·4375	11·112	15/16	0·9375	23·812
29/64	0·4531	11·509	61/64	0·9531	24·209
15/32	0·4687	11·906	31/32	0·9688	24·606
31/64	0·4844	12·303	63/64	0·9844	25·003
1/2	0·5000	12·700	1	1·0000	25·400

POWERS AND ROOTS OF π AND g

n	$\dfrac{1}{n}$	n^2	n^3	$\sqrt{n}$	$\dfrac{1}{\sqrt{n}}$	$\sqrt[3]{n}$	$\dfrac{1}{\sqrt[3]{n}}$
$\pi =$ 3·142	0·318	9·870	31·006	1·772	0·564	1·465	0·683
$2\pi =$ 6·283	0·159	39·478	248·050	2·507	0·399	1·845	0·542
$\dfrac{\pi}{2} =$ 1·571	0·637	2·467	3·878	1·253	0·798	1·102	0·860
$\dfrac{\pi}{3} =$ 1·047	0·955	1·097	1·148	1·023	0·977	1·016	0·985
$\dfrac{4\pi}{3} =$ 4·189	0·239	17·546	73·496	2·047	0·489	1·612	0·622
$\dfrac{\pi}{4} =$ 0·785	1·274	0·617	0·484	0·886	1·128	0·923	1·084
$\dfrac{\pi}{6} =$ 0·524	1·910	0·274	0·144	0·724	1·382	0·806	1·241
$\pi^2 =$ 9·870	0·101	97·409	961·390	3·142	0·318	2·145	0·466
$\pi^3 =$ 31·006	0·032	961·390	29,809·910	5·568	1·796	3·142	0·318
$\dfrac{32}{\pi} =$ 10·186	0·098	0·0005	0·001	0·313	3·192	0·461	2·168
$g =$ 32·2	0·031	1036·84	33,386·24	5·674	0·176	3·181	0·314
$2g =$ 64·4	0·015	4147·36	267,090	8·025	0·125	4·007	0·249

POWERS AND ROOTS

No.	Squares	Cubes	Square Roots	Cube Roots
1	1	1	1.000	1.000
2	4	8	1.414	1.260
3	9	27	1.732	1.442
4	16	64	2.000	1.587
5	25	125	2.236	1.710
6	36	216	2.449	1.817
7	49	343	2.646	1.913
8	64	512	2.828	2.000
9	81	729	3.000	2.080
10	100	1,000	3.162	2.154
11	121	1,331	3.317	2.224
12	144	1,728	3.464	2.289
13	169	2,197	3.606	2.351
14	196	2,744	3.742	2.410
15	225	3,375	3.873	2.466
16	256	4,096	4.000	2.520
17	289	4,913	4.123	2.571
18	324	5,832	4.243	2.621
19	361	6,859	4.359	2.668
20	400	8,000	4.472	2.714
21	441	9,261	4.583	2.759
22	484	10,648	4.690	2.802
23	529	12,167	4.796	2.844
24	576	13,824	4.899	2.884
25	625	15,625	5.000	2.924
26	676	17,576	5.099	2.962
27	729	19,683	5.196	3.000
28	784	21,952	5.292	3.037
29	841	24,389	5.385	3.072
30	900	27,000	5.477	3.107
31	961	29,791	5.568	3.141
32	1,024	32,768	5.657	3.175
33	1,089	35,937	5.745	3.208
34	1,156	39,304	5.831	3.240
35	1,225	42,875	5.916	3.271

No.	Squares	Cubes	Square Roots	Cube Roots
36	1,296	46,656	6·000	3·302
37	1,369	50,653	6·083	3·332
38	1,444	54,872	6·164	3·362
39	1,521	59,319	6·245	3·391
40	1,600	64,000	6·325	3·420
41	1,681	68,921	6·403	3·448
42	1,764	74,088	6·471	3·476
43	1,849	79,507	6·557	3·503
44	1,936	85,184	6·633	3·530
45	2,025	91,125	6·708	3·557
46	2,116	97,336	6·782	3·583
47	2,209	103,823	6·856	3·609
48	2,304	110,592	6·928	3·634
49	2,401	117,649	7·000	3·659
50	2,500	125,000	7·071	3·684
51	2,601	132,651	7·141	3·708
52	2,704	140,608	7·211	3·733
53	2,809	148,877	7·280	3·756
54	2,916	157,464	7·348	3·780
55	3,025	166,375	7·416	3·803
56	3,136	175,616	7·483	3·826
57	3,249	185,193	7·550	3·849
58	3,364	195,112	7·616	3·871
59	3,481	205,379	7·681	3·893
60	3,600	216,000	7·746	3·915
61	3,721	226,981	7·810	3·936
62	3,844	238,328	7·874	3·958
63	3,969	250,047	7·937	3·979
64	4,096	262,144	8·000	4·000
65	4,225	274,625	8·062	4·021
66	4,356	287,496	8·124	4·041
67	4,489	300,763	8·185	4·062
68	4,624	314,432	8·246	4·082
69	4,761	328,509	8·307	4·102

POWERS AND ROOTS—continued

No.	Squares	Cubes	Square Roots	Cube Roots
70	4,900	343,000	8.367	4.121
71	5,041	357,911	8.426	4.141
72	5,184	373,248	8.485	4.160
73	5,329	389,017	8.544	4.179
74	5,476	405,224	8.602	4.198
75	5,625	421,875	8.660	4.217
76	5,776	438,976	8.718	4.236
77	5,929	456,533	8.775	4.254
78	6,084	474,552	8.832	4.273
79	6,241	493,039	8.888	4.291
80	6,400	512,000	8.944	4.309
81	6,561	531,441	9.000	4.327
82	6,724	551,368	9.055	4.344
83	6,889	571,787	9.110	4.362
84	7,056	592,704	9.165	4.380
85	7,225	614,125	9.220	4.397
86	7,396	636,056	9.274	4.414
87	7,569	658,503	9.327	4.431
88	7,744	681,472	9.381	4.448
89	7,921	704,969	9.434	4.465
90	8,100	729,000	9.487	4.481
91	8,281	753,571	9.539	4.498
92	8,464	778,688	9.592	4.514
93	8,649	804,357	9.644	4.531
94	8,836	830,584	9.695	4.547
95	9,025	857,375	9.747	4.563
96	9,216	884,736	9.798	4.579
97	9,409	912,673	9.849	4.595
98	9,604	941,192	9.899	4.610
99	9,801	970,299	9.950	4.626
100	10,000	1,000,000	10.000	4.642

Centigrade—Fahrenheit Conversion Table

C.	F.	C.	F.	C.	F.	C.	F.	C.	F.	C.	F.
0	32	170	338	340	644	510	950	680	1,256	850	1,562
5	41	175	347	345	653	515	959	685	1,265	855	1,571
10	50	180	356	350	662	520	968	690	1,274	860	1,580
15	59	185	365	355	671	525	977	695	1,283	865	1,589
20	68	190	374	360	680	530	986	700	1,292	870	1,598
25	77	195	383	365	689	535	995	705	1,301	875	1,607
30	86	200	392	370	698	540	1,004	710	1,310	880	1,616
35	93	205	401	375	707	545	1,013	715	1,319	885	1,625
40	104	210	410	380	716	550	1,022	720	1,328	890	1,634
45	113	215	419	385	725	555	1,031	725	1,337	895	1,643
50	122	220	428	390	734	560	1,040	730	1,346	900	1,652
55	131	225	437	395	743	565	1,049	735	1,355	905	1,661
60	140	230	446	400	752	570	1,058	740	1,364	910	1,670
65	149	235	455	405	761	575	1,067	745	1,373	915	1,679
70	158	240	464	410	770	580	1,076	750	1,382	920	1,688
75	167	245	473	415	779	585	1,085	755	1,391	925	1,697
80	176	250	482	420	788	590	1,094	760	1,400	930	1,706
85	185	255	491	425	797	595	1,103	765	1,409	935	1,715
90	194	260	500	430	806	600	1,112	770	1,418	940	1,724
95	203	265	509	435	815	605	1,121	775	1,427	945	1,733
100	212	270	518	440	824	610	1,130	780	1,436	950	1,742
105	221	275	527	445	833	615	1,139	785	1,445	955	1,751
110	230	280	536	450	842	620	1,148	790	1,454	960	1,760
115	239	285	545	455	851	625	1,157	795	1,463	965	1,769
120	248	290	554	460	860	630	1,166	800	1,472	970	1,778
125	257	295	563	465	869	635	1,175	805	1,481	975	1,787
130	266	300	572	470	877	640	1,184	810	1,490	980	1,796
135	275	305	581	475	887	645	1,193	815	1,499	985	1,805
140	284	310	590	480	896	650	1,202	820	1,508	990	1,814
145	293	315	599	485	905	655	1,211	825	1,517	995	1,823
150	302	320	608	490	914	660	1,220	830	1,526	1,000	1,832
155	311	325	617	495	923	665	1,229	835	1,535	1,005	1,841
160	320	330	626	500	932	670	1,238	840	1,544	1,010	1,850
165	329	335	635	505	941	675	1,247	845	1,553	1,015	1,859

Temperature Conversion Formulae

°F. to °C.	.	.	.	°C. $= 5/9$ (°F. $- 32$)
°C. to °F.	.	.	.	°F. $= 9/5$ °C. $+ 32$
°F. to °R.	.	.	.	°R. $= 4/9$ (°F. $- 32$)
°R. to °F.	.	.	.	°F. $= 9/4$ °R. $+ 32$
°R. to °C.	.	.	.	°C. $= 5/4$ °R.

Absolute zero $= -273 \cdot 14$° C.

SCREWS,
BRITISH ASSOCIATION (B.A.)

No.	Absolute Dimensions in Millimetres		Approximate Number of Threads per Inch	Approximate Dimensions in Inches	
	Full Diameter	Pitch		Full Diameter	Pitch
25	0·25	0·070	362·8	0·010	0·0028
24	0·29	0·080	317·5	0·011	0·0031
23	0·33	0·09	282·2	0·013	0·0035
22	0·37	0·10	254·0	0·015	0·0039
21	0·42	0·11	230·9	0·017	0·0043
20	0·48	0·12	211·6	0·019	0·0047
19	0·54	0·14	181·4	0·021	0·0055
18	0·62	0·15	169·3	0·024	0·0059
17	0·70	0·17	149·4	0·028	0·0067
16	0·79	0·19	133·7	0·031	0·0075
15	0·90	0·21	121·0	0·035	0·0083
14	1·0	0·23	110·4	0·039	0·0091
13	1·2	0·25	101·6	0·047	0·0098
12	1·3	0·28	90·7	0·051	0·0110
11	1·5	0·31	81·9	0·059	0·0122
10	1·7	0·35	72·6	0·067	0·0138
9	1·9	0·39	65·1	0·075	0·0154
8	2·2	0·43	59·1	0·087	0·0169
7	2·5	0·48	52·9	0·098	0·0189
6	2·8	0·53	47·9	0·110	0·0209
5	3·2	0·59	43·0	0·126	0·0232
4	3·6	0·66	38·5	0·142	0·0260
3	4·1	0·73	34·8	0·161	0·0287
2	4·7	0·81	31·4	0·185	0·0319
1	5·3	0·90	28·2	0·209	0·0354
0	6·0	1·00	25·4	0·236	0·0394

It is recommended that for screws less than ¼ in. diameter British Association Threads should be adopted. It was originally proposed by the British Association in 1884, and finally adopted by them in 1904. It is, however, not yet the usual practice in this country to use the sizes ranging from No. 17 upwards. Moreover, makers of taps, dies, screwplates, etc., usually supply sizes to No. 16.

STANDARD WIRE GAUGE AND STANDARD DRILL SIZES

Standard wire gauge	Standard drill size in. mm	Decimal inch equivalent	Nearest obsolete number drill	Standard wire gauge	Standard drill size in. mm	Decimal inch equivalent	Nearest obsolete number drill
50		0·0010		34		0·0092	
49		0·0012		33		0·0100	
48		0·0016		32		0·0108	
47		0·0020		31		0·0116	
46		0·0024		30		0·0124	
45		0·0028			0·32	0·0126	
44		0·0032		29		0·0136	
43		0·0036			0·35	0·0138	80
42		0·0040		28		0·0148	
41		0·0044			0·38	0·0150	79
40		0·0048			1/64	0·0156	
39		0·0052			0·40	0·0157	78
38		0·0060		27		0·0164	
37		0·0068			0·42	0·0165	
36		0·0076			0·45	0·0177	77
35		0·0084		26		0·0180	

STANDARD WIRE GAUGE AND STANDARD DRILL SIZES—*continued*

Standard wire gauge	Standard drill size in.	mm	Decimal inch equivalent	Nearest obsolete number drill
		0·48	0·0189	76
		0·50	0·0197	
25			0·0200	
		0·52	0·0205	75
		0·55	0·0217	
24			0·0220	
		0·58	0·0228	74
		0·60	0·0236	73
23			0·0240	
		0·62	0·0244	
		0·65	0·0256	72, 71
		0·68	0·0268	
		0·70	0·0276	70
22			0·0280	
		0·72	0·0283	
		0·75	0·0295	69
		0·78	0·0307	68
	1/32		0·0312	
		0·80	0·0315	
21			0·0320	
		0·82	0·0323	67
		0·85	0·0335	66
		0·88	0·0346	
		0·90	0·0354	65
20			0·0360	
		0·92	0·0362	64
		0·95	0·0374	63
		0·98	0·0386	62
		1·00	0·0394	61, 60
19			0·0400	
		1·05	0·0413	59, 58
		1·10	0·0433	57

STANDARD WIRE GAUGE AND STANDARD DRILL SIZES—continued

Standard wire gauge	Standard drill size in.	Standard drill size mm	Decimal inch equivalent	Nearest obsolete number drill	Standard wire gauge	Standard drill size in.	Standard drill size mm	Decimal inch equivalent	Nearest obsolete number drill
		1·15	0·0453				1·70	0·0669	51
	3/64		0·0469	56			1·75	0·0689	
		1·20	0·0472				1·80	0·0709	50
18			0·0480		15			0·0720	
		1·25	0·0492				1·85	0·0728	49
		1·30	0·0512	55			1·90	0·0748	
		1·35	0·0532				1·95	0·0768	48
		1·40	0·0551	54		5/64		0·0781	
17			0·0560				2·00	0·0787	47
		1·45	0·0571		14			0·0800	
		1·50	0·0591	53			2·05	0·0807	46
		1·55	0·0610				2·10	0·0827	45
	1/16		0·0625				2·15	0·0846	
		1·60	0·0630	52			2·20	0·0866	44
16			0·0640				2·25	0·0886	43
		1·65	0·0650				2·30	0·0906	

STANDARD WIRE GAUGE AND STANDARD DRILL SIZES—continued

Standard wire gauge	Standard drill size in.	Standard drill size mm	Decimal inch equivalent	Nearest obsolete number drill
13			0·0920	
		2·35	0·0925	
	3/32		0·0938	42
		2·40	0·0945	
		2·45	0·0965	41
		2·50	0·0984	40
		2·55	0·1004	39
		2·60	0·1024	38
12			0·1040	
		2·65	0·1043	37
		2·70	0·1063	36
		2·75	0·1083	
	7/64		0·1094	35, 34
		2·80	0·1102	
		2·85	0·1122	33
		2·90	0·1142	
11			0·1160	32
		2·95	0·1161	31
		3·00	0·1181	
		3·10	0·1220	
10	1/8		0·1250	
		3·20	0·1260	
			0·1280	30
		3·30	0·1299	
		3·40	0·1339	29
		3·50	0·1378	28
	9/64		0·1406	
		3·60	0·1417	
9			0·1440	27, 26
		3·70	0·1457	25
		3·80	0·1496	24, 23
		3·90	0·1535	

Standard wire gauge	Standard drill size in.	Standard drill size mm	Decimal inch equivalent	Nearest obsolete number drill
	5/32		0·1562	
		4·00	0·1575	22, 21
8			0·1600	
		4·10	0·1614	20
		4·20	0·1654	19
		4·30	0·1693	18
	11/64		0·1719	
		4·40	0·1732	17
7			0·1760	
		4·50	0·1772	16
		4·60	0·1811	15, 14
		4·70	0·1850	13
	3/16		0·1875	
		4·80	0·1890	12
6			0·1920	
		4·90	0·1929	11, 10
		5·00	0·1968	9
		5·10	0·2008	8, 7
	13/64		0·2031	
		5·20	0·2047	6, 5
		5·30	0·2087	4
5			0·2120	
		5·40	0·2126	3
		5·50	0·2165	
	7/32		0·2188	
		5·60	0·2205	2
		5·70	0·2244	
		5·80	0·2283	1
4			0·2320	
		5·90	0·2323	
	15/64		0·2344	A
		6·00	0·2362	B

STANDARD WIRE GAUGE AND STANDARD DRILL SIZES—continued

Standard wire gauge	Standard drill size in.	Standard drill size mm	Decimal inch equivalent	Nearest obsolete letter drill
		6·10	0·2402	
		6·20	0·2441	C
		6·30	0·2480	D
	¼		0·2500	E
3		6·40	0·2520	
		6·50	0·2559	F
		6·60	0·2598	G
		6·70	0·2638	
	17/64		0·2656	H
		6·80	0·2677	
		6·90	0·2717	I
		7·00	0·2756	J
2			0·2760	
		7·10	0·2795	
	9/32		0·2812	K
		7·20	0·2835	
		7·30	0·2874	
		7·40	0·2913	L
		7·50	0·2953	M
	19/64		0·2969	

Standard wire gauge	Standard drill size in.	Standard drill size mm	Decimal inch equivalent	Nearest obsolete letter drill
		7·60	0·2992	
1			0·3000	
		7·70	0·3032	N
		7·80	0·3071	
		7·90	0·3110	
	5/16		0·3125	
		8·00	0·3150	O
		8·10	0·3189	
		8·20	0·3228	P
0			0·3240	
		8·30	0·3268	
	21/64		0·3281	
		8·40	0·3307	Q
		8·50	0·3346	
		8·60	0·3386	R
		8·70	0·3425	
	11/32		0·3438	
		8·80	0·3465	
00			0·3480	S
		8·90	0·3504	

Standard wire gauge	Standard drill size		Decimal inch equivalent	Nearest obsolete letter drill
	in.	mm		
		9·00	0·3543	
		9·10	0·3583	T
	$\frac{23}{64}$		0·3594	
		9·20	0·3622	
		9·30	0·3661	U
		9·40	0·3701	
3/0			0·3720	
		9·50	0·3740	
	$\frac{3}{8}$		0·3750	
		9·60	0·3780	V
		9·70	0·3819	
		9·80	0·3858	W
		9·90	0·3898	
	$\frac{25}{64}$		0·3906	
		10·00	0·3937	
		10·10	0·3976	X
4/0			0·4000	
		10·20	0·4016	
		10·30	0·4055	Y
	$\frac{13}{32}$		0·4062	
		10·40	0·4094	
		10·50	0·4134	Z
		10·60	0·4173	
		10·70	0·4213	
	$\frac{27}{64}$		0·4219	
		10·80	0·4252	
		10·90	0·4291	
5/0			0·4320	
		11·00	0·4331	
		11·10	0·4370	
	$\frac{7}{16}$		0·4375	
		11·20	0·4409	

Drill sizes proceed thus:
$\frac{1}{8}$ to 2 in. in $\frac{1}{64}$ in. steps;
12·7 to 14 mm in 0·1 mm steps;
14 to 25 mm in 0·25 mm steps;
25 to 50·5 mm in 0·5 mm steps.

B.S.I. STANDARD METRIC SIZES OF COPPER WINDING WIRES

| Conductor diameter | | | Sectional area | Weight per km | Nominal resistance at 20°C | | Current rating at 4·65 amps per mm²† |
Nom mm	Max mm	Min mm	mm²	kg	Per metre ohms	Per kg ohms	amps
5·000	5·050	4·950	19·63	174·6	0·0008781	0·005029	91·30
4·750	4·798	4·702	17·72	157·5	0·0009781	0·006178	82·40
4·500	4·545	4·455	15·90	141·4	0·001084	0·007666	73·95
4·250	4·293	4·207	14·19	126·1	0·001215	0·009635	65·96
4·000	4·040	3·960	12·57	111·7	0·001372	0·01228	58·43
3·750	3·788	3·712	11·04	98·19	0·001561	0·01590	51·36
3·550	3·586	3·514	9·898	87·99	0·001742	0·01980	46·03
3·350	3·384	3·316	8·814	78·36	0·001956	0·02496	40·99
3·150	3·182	3·118	7·793	69·28	0·002212	0·03193	36·24
3·000	3·030	2·970	7·069	62·84	0·002439	0·03881	32·87
2·800	2·828	2·772	6·158	54·74	0·002800	0·05115	28·63
2·650	2·677	2·623	5·515	49·03	0·003126	0·06370	25·65
2·500	2·525	2·475	4·909	43·64	0·003512	0·08048	22·83
2·360	2·384	2·336	4·374	38·89	0·003941	0·1013	20·34
2·240	2·262	2·218	3·941	35·03	0·004375	0·1249	18·32
2·120	2·141	2·099	3·530	31·38	0·004884	0·1556	16·41
2·000	2·020	1·980	3·142	27·93	0·005488	0·1965	14·61
1·900	1·919	1·881	2·835	25·21	0·006081	0·2412	13·18
1·800	1·818	1·782	2·545	22·62	0·006775	0·2996	11·83
1·700	1·717	1·683	2·270	20·18	0·007396	0·3764	10·55

† 4·65 amps per mm² is equivalent to 3,000 amps per in².
Preferred sizes shown in heavy print.

Nom mm	Conductor diameter		Sectional area mm²	Weight per Km kg	Nominal resistance at 20°C		Current rating at 4·65 amps per mm²† amps
	Max mm	Min mm			Per metre ohms	Per kg ohms	
1·600	1·616	1·584	2·011	17·87	0·008575	0·4799	9·349
1·500	1·515	1·485	1·767	15·71	0·009757	0·6211	8·217
1·400	1·414	1·386	1·539	13·69	0·01120	0·8181	7·158
1·320	1·333	1·307	1·368	12·17	0·01260	1·035	6·364
1·250	1·263	1·237	1·227	10·91	0·01405	1·288	5·706
1·180	1·192	1·168	1·094	9·722	0·01577	1·622	5·085
1·120	1·131	1·109	0·9852	8·758	0·01750	1·998	4·581
1·060	1·071	1·049	0·8825	7·845	0·01954	2·491	4·103
1·000	1·010	0·990	0·7854	6·982	0·02195	3·144	3·652
0·950	0·960	0·940	0·7088	6·301	0·02432	3·860	3·296
0·900	0·909	0·891	0·6362	5·656	0·02710	4·791	2·958
0·850	0·859	0·841	0·5675	5·045	0·03038	6·022	2·639
0·800	0·808	0·792	0·5027	4·469	0·03430	7·675	2·337
0·750	0·758	0·742	0·4418	3·928	0·03903	9·938	2·054
0·710	0·717	0·703	0·3959	3·520	0·04355	12·37	1·841
0·670	0·677	0·663	0·3526	3·134	0·04890	15·60	1·639
0·630	0·636	0·624	0·3117	2·771	0·05531	19·96	1·449
0·600	0·606	0·594	0·2827	2·514	0·06098	24·26	1·315
0·560	0·566	0·554	0·2463	2·190	0·07000	31·96	1·145
0·530	0·536	0·524	0·2206	1·961	0·07814	39·85	1·026

† 4·65 amps per mm² is equivalent to 3,000 amps per in².
Preferred sizes shown in heavy print.

B.S.I. STANDARD METRIC SIZES OF COPPER WINDING WIRES—cont.

| Conductor diameter | | | Sectional area | Weight per km | Nominal resistance at 20°C | | Current rating at 4·65 amps per mm² |
Nom mm	Max mm	Min mm	mm²	kg	Per metre ohms	Per kg ohms	amps
0·500	0·505	0·495	0·1963	1·746	0·08781	50·29	0·9130
0·475	0·480	0·470	0·1772	1·575	0·09730	61·78	0·8240
0·450	0·455	0·445	0·1590	1·414	0·1084	76·66	0·7395
0·425	0·430	0·420	0·1419	1·261	0·1215	96·35	0·6596
0·400	0·405	0·395	0·1257	1·117	0·1372	122·8	0·5843
0·375	0·380	0·370	0·1104	0·9819	0·1561	159·0	0·5136
0·355	0·359	0·351	0·09898	0·8799	0·1742	198·0	0·4603
0·335	0·339	0·331	0·08814	0·7836	0·1956	249·6	0·4099
0·315	0·319	0·311	0·07793	0·6928	0·2212	319·3	0·3624
0·300	0·304	0·296	0·07069	0·6284	0·2439	388·1	0·3287
0·280	0·284	0·276	0·06158	0·5474	0·2800	511·5	0·2863
0·265	0·269	0·261	0·05515	0·4903	0·3126	637·6	0·2565
0·250	0·254	0·246	0·04909	0·4364	0·3512	804·8	0·2283
0·236	0·240	0·232	0·04374	0·3889	0·3941	1,013·0	0·2034
0·224	0·227	0·221	0·03941	0·3503	0·4375	1,249·0	0·1832
0·212	0·215	0·209	0·03530	0·3138	0·4884	1,556·0	0·1641
0·200	0·203	0·197	0·03142	0·2793	0·5488	1,965·0	0·1461
0·190	0·193	0·187	0·02835	0·2521	0·6081	2,421·0	0·1318
0·180	0·183	0·177	0·02545	0·2262	0·6775	2,995·0	0·1183
0·170	0·173	0·167	0·02270	0·2018	0·7596	3,764·0	0·1055

† 4·65 amps per mm² is equivalent to 3,000 amps per in².
Preferred sizes shown in heavy print.

B.S.I. STANDARD METRIC SIZES OF COPPER WINDING WIRES —cont.

Nom mm	Conductor diameter			Sectional area mm²	Weight per km kg	Nominal resistance at 20°C		Current rating at 4·65 amps per mm²† amps
	Max mm	Min mm				Per metre ohms	Per kg ohms	
0·160	0·163	0·157		0·02011	0·1787	0·8575	4,799·0	0·0935
0·150	0·153	0·147		0·01767	0·1571	0·9757	6,211·0	0·0822
0·140	0·143	0·137		0·01539	0·1369	1·120	8,181·0	0·0716
0·132	0·135	0·129		0·01368	0·1217	1·260	10,353·0	0·0636
0·125	0·128	0·122		0·01227	0·1091	1·405	12,878·0	0·0571
0·112	0·109			0·009852	0·08758	1·750	19,982·0	0·0458
0·100	0·103	0·097		0·007854	0·06982	2·195	31,438·0	0·0365
0·090	0·093	0·087		0·006362	0·05656	2·710	47,914·0	0·0296
0·080	0·083	0·077		0·005027	0·04469	3·430	76,751·0	0·0234
0·071	0·074	0·068		0·003959	0·03520	4·355	123,722·0	0·0184
0·083	—			0·003117	0·02771	5·531	199,603·0	0·0145
0·060	—			0·002827	0·02514	6·098	242,562·0	0·0132
0·056	—			0·002463	0·02190	7·000	319,635·0	0·0115
0·050	—			0·001963	0·01746	8·781	502,921·0	0·0091
0·045	—			0·001590	0·01414	10·84	766,620·0	0·0074
0·040	—			0·001257	0·01117	13·72	1,228,290·0	0·0068
0·036	—			0·001018	0·009049	16·94	1,870,460·0	0·0047
0·032	—			0·0008042	0·007150	21·44	2,998,601·0	0·0037
0·032	—			0·0007069	0·006284	24·39	3,881,286·0	0·0033
0·028	—			0·0006158	0·005474	28·00	5,115,090·0	0·0029
0·025	—			0·0004909	0·004364	35·12	8,047,663·0	0·0023

† 4·65 amps per mm² is equivalent to 3,000 amps per in².
Preferred sizes shown in heavy print.

METRIC WIRE SIZES: TURNS
PER 10 mm

Nominal bare diameter mm	Turns per 10 mm min	Nominal bare diameter mm	Turns per 10 mm min
5·000	1·9	**0·500**	18·3
4·750	2·0	0·475	19·2
4·500	2·2	**0·450**	20·2
4·250	2·3	0·425	21·3
4·000	2·4	**0·400**	22·6
3·750	2·6	0·375	24·0
3·550	2·7	**0·355**	25·3
3·350	2·9	0·335	26·7
3·150	3·1	**0·315**	28·4
3·000	3·2	0·300	29·7
2·800	3·4	**0·280**	31·8
2·650	3·6	0·265	33·3
2·500	3·8	**0·250**	35·2
2·360	4·1	0·236	37·2
2·240	4·3	**0·224**	39·1
2·120	4·5	0·212	41·2
2·000	4·8	**0·200**	43·5
1·900	5·0	0·190	45·5
1·800	5·3	**1·180**	47·9
1·700	5·6	0·170	50·5
1·600	5·9	**0·160**	53·5
1·500	6·3	0·150	56·5
1·400	6·8	**0·140**	60·2
1·320	7·2	0·132	63·7
1·250	7·5	**0·125**	67·1
1·180	8·0	**0·112**	74·6
1·120	8·4	**0·100**	82·6
1·060	8·8	0·090	90·9
1·000	9·4	**0·080**	102·0
0·950	9·9	0·071	113·6
0·900	10·4	**0·063**	128·2
0·850	11·0	0·060	133·3
0·800	11·6	0·056	142·9
0·750	12·4	**0·050**	161·3
0·710	13·0	0·045	178·6
0·670	13·8	**0·040**	200·0
0·630	14·6	0·036	222·2
0·600	15·3	**0·032**	250·0
0·560	16·4	0·030	263·2
0·530	17·3	0·028	285·7
		0·025	322·6

Preferred sizes shown in heavy print.

COPPER WIRE DATA (S.W.G.)

Standard Wire Gauge	Diameter in Inches	Resistance in Ohms per Yard	Resistance in Ohms per Pound	Pounds per Ohm	Weight in Pounds per 1,000 Yards	Yards per Pound	Turns per Inch — Enamel Covered	Single Silk Covered	Double Silk Covered	Single Cotton Covered	Double Cotton Covered
10	0·128	0·001368	0·01200	83·3	148·8	6·67	←	7·64	7·55	7·35	7·04
11	0·116	0·001665	0·02000	50·0	122·2	8·16		8·41	8·30	8·06	7·69
12	0·104	0·002080	0·02801	35·7	98·22	10·23		9·35	9·22	8·93	8·48
13	0·092	0·002660	0·0553	18·1	76·86	13·00		10·5	10·4	9·93	9·43
14	0·080	0·003512	0·0882	11·3	58·12	17·16		12·1	11·8	11·4	10·6
15	0·072	0·004339	0·1401	7·14	47·08	21·23		13·3	13·1	12·5	11·6
16	0·064	0·005491	0·2021	4·95	37·20	26·86	15·0	14·9	14·6	13·9	13·2
17	0·056	0·007170	0·3423	2·92	28·48	35·00	17·1	16·9	16·5	15·9	14·7
18	0·048	0·009762	0·6351	1·575	20·92	47·66	19·8	19·8	19·4	18·5	17·2
19	0·040	0·01406	1·324	0·755	14·53	68·80	23·7	23·7	23·0	21·7	20·0
20	0·036	0·01735	2·012	0·497	11·77	85·00	26·9	26·3	25·3	23·8	21·7
21	0·032	0·02196	3·233	0·309	9·299	107·6	30·4	30·4	28·6	26·8	24·3
22	0·028	0·02868	5·516	0·181	7·120	140·6	33·8	33·8	31·8	29·4	26·9
23	0·024	0·03905	10·14	0·0986	5·231	191·6	38·8	38·8	36·4	33·3	29·3
24	0·022	0·04646	14·47	0·0691	4·395	228·3	42·1	42·1	38·5	33·5	29·3
25	0·020	0·05622	21·19	0·0472	3·633	275·3	46·0	46·0	43·5	38·5	33·3
26	0·018	0·06941	32·30	0·0310	2·942	340·0	50·6	50·6	47·6	41·7	33·3
27	0·0164	0·08362	46·86	0·0213	2·442	410·0	55·9	55·1	51·6	44·6	37·9

163

COPPER WIRE DATA (S.W.G.)—continued

Standard Wire Gauge	Diameter in Inches	Resistance in Ohms per Yard	Resistance in Ohms per Pound	Pounds per Ohm	Weight in Pounds per 1,000 Yards	Yards per Pound	Turns per Inch				
							Enamel Covered	Single Silk Covered	Double Silk Covered	Single Cotton Covered	Double Cotton Covered
28	0·0148	0·1398	70·12	0·0141	1·989	503·0	61·4	60·4	56·2	48·1	40·2
29	0·0136	0·1655	98·65	0·0101	1·680	596·6	66·2	65·2	60·2	51·0	42·4
30	0·0124	0·1991	142·75	0·0069	1·396	716·6	73·3	72·0	67·1	54·4	44·7
31	0·0116	0·2275	185·80	0·0054	1·222	820·0	77·8	76·3	70·9	56·8	46·3
32	0·0108	0·2625	248·20	0·0040	1·059	943·3	83·0	81·3	75·2	63·3	50·5
33	0·0100	0·3061	337·50	0·0029	0·9081	1,100	88·9	87·0	80·5	66·7	52·6
34	0·0092	0·3617	471·00	0·0023	0·7686	1,300	98·0	93·4	89·5	70·4	54·9
35	0·0084	0·4338	676·50	0·0015	0·6403	1,556	106	101	91·8	80·6	64·1
36	0·0076	0·5300	1,076	0·00098	0·5284	1,903	116	110	103	86·2	67·6
37	0·0068	0·6620	1,574	0·00064	0·4199	2,380	128	120	110	92·6	71·4
38	0·0060	0·8503	2,598	0·000385	0·3269	3,056	143	133	121	100	75·8
39	0·0052	1·132	4,645	0·000217	0·2456	4,066	168	149	134	109	78·1
40	0·0048	1·328	6,360	0·000156	0·2092	4,766	180	159	142	144	
41	0·0044	1·581	9,020	0·000112	0·1753	5,700	194	169	150		
42	0·0040	1·913	13,150	0·000076	0·1453	6,866	211	191	167		
43	0·0036	2·362	20,120	0·000050	0·1177	7,500	230	206	179		
44	0·0032	2·989	32,210	0·000030	0·0929	10,766	253	225	193		
45	0·0028	3·904	54,980	0·000015	0·0713	14,066	283	247	208		

WIRE GAUGES—1

Number of Gauge	S.W.G.		A.W.G. or B.&.S.		B.W.G.		Gold and Silver (Birmingham)		Lancashire Steel Pinion Wire	
	in.	mm.	in.	mm.	in.	mm.	in.	mm.	in.	mm.
7/0	0·500	12·70	—	—	—	—	—	—	—	—
6/0	0·464	11·78	—	—	—	—	—	—	—	—
5/0	0·432	10·97	—	—	—	—	—	—	—	—
4/0	0·400	10·16	0·46	11·68	0·454	11·53	—	—	—	—
3/0	0·372	9·44	0·409	10·388	0·425	10·787	—	—	—	—
2/0	0·348	8·83	0·364	9·24	0·380	9·65	—	—	—	—
1/0	0·324	8·23	0·324	8·23	0·340	8·63	—	—	—	—
1	0·300	7·62	0·289	7·338	0·300	7·62	0·004	0·101	0·227	5·757
2	0·276	7·01	0·257	6·527	0·284	7·21	0·005	0·127	0·219	5·558
3	0·252	6·40	0·229	5·808	0·259	6·58	0·008	0·203	0·212	5·380
4	0·232	5·89	0·204	5·18	0·238	6·04	0·010	0·254	0·207	5·257
5	0·212	5·38	0·181	4·59	0·220	5·58	0·012	0·304	0·204	5·187
6	0·192	4·88	0·162	4·11	0·203	5·156	0·013	0·330	0·201	5·105
7	0·176	4·46	0·144	3·66	0·180	4·57	0·015	0·381	0·199	5·048
8	0·160	4·06	0·128	3·24	0·165	4·187	0·016	0·406	0·197	4·991
9	0·144	3·66	0·114	2·89	0·148	3·753	0·019	0·482	0·194	4·921
10	0·128	3·24	0·101	2·565	0·134	3·40	0·024	0·61	0·191	4·845
11	0·116	2·94	0·090	2·38	0·120	3·04	0·029	0·736	0·188	4·777
12	0·104	2·642	0·080	2·03	0·109	2·768	0·034	0·863	0·185	4·697
13	0·092	2·336	0·071	1·79	0·095	2·413	0·036	0·914	0·182	4·620
14	0·080	2·03	0·064	1·635	0·083	2·108	0·041	1·041	0·180	4·57

WIRE GAUGES—2

Number of Gauge	S.W.G.		A.W.G. or B.&S.		B.W.G.		Gold and Silver (Birmingham)		Lancashire Steel Pinion Wire	
	in.	mm.	in.	mm.	in.	mm.	in.	mm.	in.	mm.
15	0·072	1·828	0·057	1·447	0·072	1·828	0·047	1·143	0·178	4·513
16	0·064	1·625	0·050	1·27	0·065	1·65	0·051	1·295	0·175	4·437
17	0·056	1·422	0·045	1·14	0·058	1·473	0·057	1·447	0·172	4·360
18	0·048	1·219	0·040	1·016	0·049	1·244	0·061	1·549	0·168	4·263
19	0·040	1·016	0·035	0·889	0·042	1·066	0·064	1·625	0·164	4·161
20	0·036	0·914	0·031	0·787	0·035	0·889	0·067	1·701	0·161	4·085
21	0·032	0·812	0·028	0·711	0·032	0·813	0·072	1·828	0·157	3·988
22	0·028	0·711	0·025	0·635	0·028	0·711	0·074	1·879	0·155	3·937
23	0·024	0·61	0·022	0·558	0·025	0·635	0·077	1·955	0·153	3·886
24	0·022	0·558	0·020	0·508	0·022	0·558	0·082	2·082	0·151	3·835
25	0·020	0·508	0·017	0·431	0·020	0·508	0·095	2·413	0·148	3·753
26	0·018	0·457	0·015	0·381	0·018	0·457	0·103	2·616	0·146	3·702
27	0·016	0·406	0·0148	0·376	0·016	0·406	0·113	2·87	0·143	3·626
28	0·0148	0·376	0·012	0·304	0·0148	0·376	0·120	3·04	0·139	3·528
29	0·0136	0·345	0·0116	0·29	0·0136	0·345	0·124	3·15	0·134	3·401
30	0·012	0·304	0·010	0·254	0·012	0·304	0·126	3·193	0·127	3·217
31	0·0116	0·29	0·008	0·203	0·010	0·254	0·133	3·376	0·120	3·04
32	0·0108	0·274	0·0079	0·199	0·009	0·228	0·143	3·626	0·115	2·917
33	0·010	0·254	0·007	0·177	0·008	0·203	0·145	3·677	0·112	2·840
34	0·009	0·228	0·006	0·152	0·0076	0·193	0·148	3·753	0·110	2·79
35	0·008	0·203	0·0056	0·142	0·005	0·127	0·158	4·013	0·108	2·743
36	0·0076	0·193	0·005	0·127	0·004	0·101	0·167	4·237	0·106	2·692

METRIC SIZES OF INSULATED ROUND WINDING WIRES

	Nominal conductor diameter	
Preferred metric size mm	*Non-preferred metric size mm*	*Approximate inch equivalent*
5·000		0·1969
4·750		0·1870
4·500		0·1772
4·250		0·1673
4·000		0·1575
3·750		0·1476
3·550		0·1398
3·350		0·1319
3·150		0·1240
3·000		0·1181
2·800		0·1102
2·650		0·1043
2·500		0·0984
2·360		0·0929
2·240		0·0882
2·120		0·0835
2·000		0·0787
1·900		0·0748
1,800		0·0709
1·700		0·0669
1·600		0·0630
1·500		0·0591
1·400		0·0551
1·320		0·0520
1·250		0·0492
1·180		0·0465
1·120		0·0441
1·060		0·0417
1·000		0·0394
0·950		0·0374
0·900		0·0354
0·850		0·0335
0·800		0·0315
0·750		0·0295
0·710		0·0280
	0·670	0·0264
0·630		0·0248
	0·600	0·0236
0·560		0·0220
	0·530	0·0209

METRIC SIZES OF INSULATED
ROUND WINDING WIRES—*continued*

Nominal conductor diameter		
Preferred metric size mm	*Non-preferred metric size mm*	*Approximate inch equivalent*
0·500		0·0197
	0·475	0·0187
0·450		0·0177
	0·425	0·0167
0·400		0·01575
	0·375	0·0148
0·355		0·0140
	0·335	0·0132
0·315		0·0124
	0·300	0·0118
0·280		0·0110
	0·265	0·0104
0·250		0·0098
	0·236	0·0093
0·224		0·0088
	0·212	0·00835
0·200		0·0079
	0·190	0·0075
0·180		0·0071
	0·170	0·0067
0·160		0·0063
	0·150	0·0059
0·140		0·0055
	0·132	0·0052
0·125		0·0049
0·112		0·00441
0·100		0·00394
0·090		0·00354
0·080		0·00315
0·071		0·00280
0·063		0·00248
	0·060	0·00236
	0·056	0·00220
0·050		0·00197
	0·045	0·00177
0·040		0·00157
	0·036	0·00142
0·032		0·00126
	0·030	0·00118
	0·028	0·00110
0·025		0·00098

FLUXES FOR SOLDERING

Metals	Fluxes	Fluxes generally used
Iron	Chloride of zinc	Chloride of zinc
Steel	Sal-ammoniac	(killed spirit)
Copper	Chloride of zinc	
Brass	{ Resin { Sal-ammoniac	Resin
Zinc (new) } Zinc (old) }	Chloride of zinc	
Lead (with fine solder)	Hydrochloric acid	
Lead (with coarse solder)	Tallow and resin	
Tin	Tallow	
Pewter	Resin or sweet oil	

COMPOSITION OF SOFT SOLDERS

Solder	Composition	Melting-point
Fine	1½ parts tin, 1 part lead	168°C
Tinman's	1 part tin, 1 part lead	188°C
Plumber's	1 part tin, 2 parts lead	227°C

A mixture of 1½ parts tin and 1 part lead fuses at a lower temperature than any other mixed proportion of these metals.

COMPOSITION OF HARD SOLDERS

Solder	Composition
Hard brazing	3 parts copper, 1 part zinc
Hard brazing	1 part copper, 1 part zinc
Softer brazing	4 parts copper, 3 parts zinc, and 1 part tin

MUSICAL NOTES FREQUENCY

The range of notes on a piano keyboard is from 27·5 Hz to 4186 Hz. Middle C (the centre note on a standard keyboard) has a frequency of 261·6 Hz. Standard pitch is A above middle C at a frequency of 440 Hz. Note that raising the pitch of a note is equivalent to doubling the frequency for each complete octave.

A 27·5	G 98·0	F 349·2	E 1318·5
B 30·9	A 110·0	G 392·0	F 1396·9
C 32·7	B 123·5	A 440·0	G 1568·0
D 36·7	C 130·8	B 493·9	A 1760·0
E 41·2	D 146·8	C 523·3	B 1975·5
F 43·7	E 164·8	D 587·3	C 2093·0
G 49·0	F 174·6	E 659·2	D 2344·3
A 55·0	G 196·0	F 698·5	E 2637·0
B 61·7	A 220·0	G 784·0	F 2793·8
C 65·4	B 246·9	A 880·0	G 3136·0
D 73·4	C 261·6	B 987·8	A 3520·0
E 82·4	D 293·7	C 1046·5	B 3951·1
F 87·3	E 329·6	D 1174·0	C 4186·0

MOTOR CURRENT TABLE

	ALTERNATING CURRENT — *Approx. amps. per phase taken by modern induction motors, allowing reasonable efficiencies and power factors*							DIRECT CURRENT — *Approx. amps. taken by D.C. motors, allowing reasonable efficiencies*				
B.H.P. of motor	Single Phase		Two Phase		Three Phase							B.H.P. of motor
	230 Volts	400 Volts	200 Volts	400 Volts	240 Volts	440 Volts	500 Volts	110 Volts	220 Volts	440 Volts	500 Volts	
⅛	1·0	0·6	0·6	0·3	0·4	0·3	0·3	1·4	0·7	0·4	0·3	⅛
¼	1·8	1·1	1·3	0·7	0·7	0·6	0·6	2·7	1·4	0·7	0·6	¼
⅓	2·5	1·5	1·5	0·8	0·8	0·7	0·7	3·5	1·7	1·0	1·0	⅓
½	3·8	2·0	2·0	1·2	1·2	1·1	1·0	5·0	2·5	1·7	1·5	½
¾	4·8	3·0	2·5	1·5	1·5	1·3	1·3	7·0	4·0	2·5	2·0	¾
1	6·2	4·0	3·3	2·0	2·0	1·7	1·5	9·0	5·0	2·5	2·5	1
1¼	7·4	4·8	4·0	2·5	2·2	2·0	1·7	12·0	6·0	3·0	3·0	1¼
1½	8·7	5·7	4·8	2·9	2·7	2·2	1·9	14·5	7·5	3·5	3·0	1½
1¾	10·0	6·3	5·5	3·0	2·8	2·3	2·2	17·0	8·5	4·0	3·5	1¾
2	11·8	7·0	6·3	3·2	3·0	2·8	2·5	19·0	9·5	4·5	3·7	2
2½	14·0	8·2	7·0	3·5	3·5	3·2	2·8	23·0	11·0	5·5	5·0	2½
3	17·5	9·5	8·5	4·3	4·0	3·5	3·2	27·0	13·0	6·5	5·5	3
4	24·0	12·0	10·0	5·0	5·0	4·3	3·6	35·0	16·5	6·5	5·5	4
5	34·0	14·0	14·0	7·0	6·0	5·0	4·2	41·0	20·0	9·5	7·5	5
7½	47·0	20·0	20·0	9·0	9·0	7·0	5·5	60·0	25·0	13·0	9·5	7½
10	59·0	27·0	26·0	13·0	13·0	11·0	10·0	73·0	39·0	19·0	13·0	10
12½	70·0	34·0	32·0	15·0	18·0	16·0	13·0	78·0	47·0	23·0	22·0	12½
15	91·0	40·0	38·0	19·0	22·0	18·0	16·0	114·0	58·0	29·0	25·0	15
20	118·0	53·0	50·0	25·0	25·0	21·0	19·0	152·0	76·0	38·0	34·0	20
30	135·0	78·0	75·0	38·0	33·0	28·0	25·0	220·0	115·0	54·0	54·0	30
40	183·0	105·0	100·0	50·0	39·0	34·0	36·0	305·0	152·0	76·0	67·0	40
50	227·0	130·0	120·0	60·0	53·0	47·0	47·0	380·0	190·0	95·0	87·0	50

Note.—In Slip-ring Motors, the voltage and current of the rotor are quite independent of those of the stator and as the rotor current may be much greater than that taken from the line, it is always advisable to ascertain its value in order that connecting rotor cables of suitable size may be provided.

MENSURATION

A and a = area; b = base; C and c = circumference; D and d = diameter; h = height; $n°$ = number of degrees; p = perpendicular; R and r = radius; s = span or chord; v = versed sine.

Square: $a = \text{side}^2$; side $= \sqrt{a}$;

diagonal = side $\times \sqrt{2}$.

Rectangle or parallelogram: $a = bp$.

Trapezoid (two sides parallel): a = mean length parallel sides × distance between them.

Triangle: $a = \frac{1}{2}bp$.

Irregular figure: a = weight of template ÷ weight of square inch of similar material.

Side of square multiplied by 1·4142 equals diameter of its circumscribing circle.

A side multiplied by 4·443 equals circumference of its circumscribing circle.

A side multiplied by 1·128 equals diameter of a circle of equal area.

Square inches multiplied by 1·273 equals square inches of an equal circle.

Circle: $a = \pi r^2 = d^2\dfrac{\pi}{4} = 0.7854d^2 = 0.5$ cr.;

$c = 2\pi r = d\pi = 3.1416d = 3.54\sqrt{a} =$ (approx.) $\frac{2\cdot2}{7}d$. Side of equal square $= 0.8862d$; side of inscribed square $= 0.7071d$; $d = 0.3183c$. A circle has the maximum area for a given perimeter.

Annulus of circle: $a = (D + d)(D - d)\dfrac{\pi}{4}$

$$= (D^2 - d^2)\dfrac{\pi}{4}.$$

Segment of circle:

$a =$ area of sector $-$ area of triangle

$$= \dfrac{4v}{3}\sqrt{(0.625v)^2 + (\tfrac{1}{2}S)^2}.$$

Length of arc $= 0.0174533n^\circ r$; length of

$$\text{arc} = \tfrac{1}{3}\Big(8\sqrt{\dfrac{S^2}{4} + v^2} - s\Big);$$

approx. length of arc $= \frac{1}{3}$ (8 times chord of $\frac{1}{2}$ arc $-$ chord of whole arc).

$$d = \dfrac{(\tfrac{1}{2}\text{ chord})}{v} + v;$$

$$\text{radius of curve} = \dfrac{S^2}{8V} + \dfrac{V}{2}.$$

Sector of circle: $a = 0.5r \times$ length arc;
$$= n^\circ \times \text{area circle} \div 360.$$

Ellipse: $a = \dfrac{\pi}{4} Dd = \pi Rr$; c (approx.)

$$= \sqrt{\dfrac{D^2 + d^2}{2}} \times \pi; \ c \ (\text{approx.}) = \pi \dfrac{Da}{2}.$$

Parabola: $a = \frac{2}{3}bh$.

Cone or pyramid: surface

$$= \dfrac{\text{circ. of base} \times \text{slant length}}{2} + \text{base};$$

contents = area of base × $\frac{1}{3}$ vertical height.

Frustum of cone:

surface = $(C + c) \times \frac{1}{2}$ slant height + ends;

contents = $0{\cdot}2618h(D^2 + d^2 + Dd)$;

$\quad = \frac{1}{3}h(A + a + \sqrt{A \times a})$.

Wedge: contents = $\frac{1}{6}$ (length of edge + 2 length of back)bh.

Oblique prism: contents = area base × height.

Sphere: surface = $d^3\pi = 4\pi r^3$;

$$\text{contents} = d^3\dfrac{\pi}{6} = \dfrac{4}{3}\pi r\text{I}.$$

Segment of sphere: $r = $ rad. of base;

contents = $\dfrac{\pi}{6}h(3r^2 + h^2)$; $r = $ rad. of sphere;

contents = $\dfrac{\pi}{3}h^2(3r - h)$.

Spherical zone:

contents = $\dfrac{\pi}{2}h(\frac{1}{3}h^2 + R^2 + r^2)$; surface of convex part of segment or zone of sphere = $\pi d(\text{of sph.})h = 2\pi rh$.

Mid. sph. zone: contents $= (r + \frac{2}{3}h^2)\frac{\pi}{4}$.

Spheroid:

contents $=$ revolving axis^2 $\times$ fixed axis $\times \frac{\pi}{6}$.

Cube or rectangular solid contents $=$ length $\times$ breadth $\times$ thickness.

Prismoidal formula: contents

$$= \frac{\text{end areas} + 4 \text{ times mid. area} \times \text{length.}}{6}$$

Solid revolution: contents $= a$ of generating plane $\times$ c described by centroid of this plane during revolution. Areas of similar plane figures are as the squares of like sides. Contents of similar solids are as the cubes of like sides.

Rules relative to the circle, square, cylinder, etc.:

To find circumference of a circle:
   Multiply diameter by 3·1416; or divide diameter by 0·3183.

To find diameter of a circle:
   Multiply circumference by 0·3183; or divide circumference by 3·1416.

To find radius of a circle:
   Multiply circumference by 0·15915; or divide circumference by 6·28318.

To find the side of an inscribed square:
   Multiply diameter by 0·7071; or multiply circumference by 0·2251; or divide circumference by 4·4428.

To find side of an equal square:
  Multiply diameter by 0·8862; or divide
  diameter by 1·1284; or multiply circumference by 0·2821; or divide circumference by 3·545.

To find area of a circle:
  Multiply circumference by $\frac{1}{4}$ of the diameter; or multiply the square of diameter by 0·7854; or multiply the square
  of circumference by 0·07958; or multiply
  the square of $\frac{1}{2}$ diameter by 3·1416.

To find the surface of a sphere or globe:
  Multiply the diameter by the circumference; or multiply the square of diameter
  by 3·1416; or multiply 4 times the square
  of radius by 3·1416.

Cylinder.
  To find the area of surface:
  Multiply the diameter by $3\frac{1}{7} \times$ length.
  Capacity $= 3\frac{1}{7} \times$ radius² × height.

Values and Powers of:
  $\pi = 3\cdot1415926536$, or $3\cdot1416$, or $\frac{22}{7}$ or $3\frac{1}{7}$;
  $\pi^2 = 9\cdot86965$; $\sqrt{\pi} = 1\cdot772453$;

  $\dfrac{1}{\pi} = 0\cdot31831$; $\dfrac{\pi}{2} = 1\cdot570796$;

  $\dfrac{\pi}{3} = 1\cdot047197$.

Radian $= 57\cdot2958$ degrees.

FIG. 1. Diagram for
Table A.

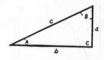

FIG. 2. Diagram for
Table B.

TABLE A

See Fig. 1

Parts Given	Parts to be Found	Formulæ
a b c	A	$\cos A = \dfrac{b^2 + c^2 - a^2}{2bc}$
a b A	B	$\sin B = \dfrac{b \times \sin A}{a}$
a b A	C	$C = 180° - (A + B)$
a A B	b	$b = \dfrac{a \times \sin B}{\sin A}$
a A B	c	$c = \dfrac{a \sin C}{\sin A} = \dfrac{a \sin (180° - A - B)}{\sin A}$
a b C	B	$B = 180° - (A + C)$

TABLE B

See Fig. 2

Parts Given	Parts to be Found: A	B	a	b	c
a & c	$\sin A - \frac{a}{c}$	$\cos B - \frac{a}{c}$		$b = \sqrt{c^2 - a^2}$	
a & b	$\tan A = \frac{a}{b}$	$\cot B = \frac{a}{b}$			$c = \sqrt{a^2 + b^2}$
c & b	$\cos A = \frac{b}{c}$	$\sin B = \frac{b}{c}$	$a = \sqrt{c^2 - b^2}$		
A & a		$B = 90° - A$		$b = a \times \cot A$	$c = \frac{a}{\sin A}$
A & b		$B = 90° - A$	$a = b \times \tan A$		$c = \frac{b}{\cos A}$
A & c		$B = 90° - A$	$a = c \times \sin A$	$b = c \times \cos A$	

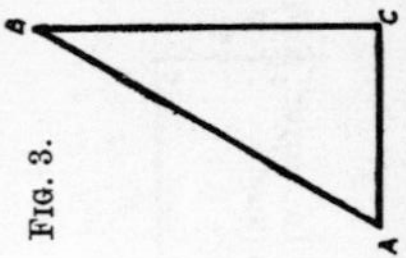

FIG. 3.

Fig. 3.—In any right-angled triangle:

$$\tan A = \frac{BC}{AC}, \quad \sin A = \frac{BC}{AB}$$

$$\cos A = \frac{AC}{AB}, \quad \cot A = \frac{AC}{BC}$$

$$\sec A = \frac{AB}{AC}, \quad \text{cosec } A = \frac{AB}{BC}$$

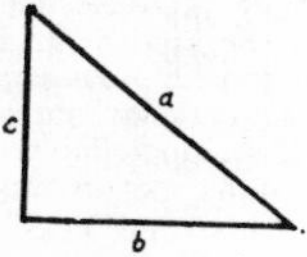

FIG. 4.

Fig. 4.—In any right-angled triangle:

$$a^2 = c^2 + b^2$$
$$c = \sqrt{a^2 - b^2}$$
$$b = \sqrt{a^2 - c^2}$$
$$a = \sqrt{b^2 + c^2}$$

Fig. 5.—$c + d : a + b :: b - a : d - c.$

$$d = \frac{c + d}{2} + \frac{d - c}{2}$$
$$x = \sqrt{b^2 - d^2}$$

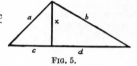

FIG. 5.

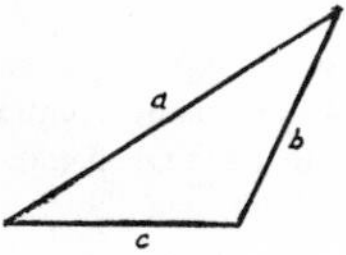

FIG. 6.

In Fig. 6, where the lengths of three sides only are known:

$$\text{area} = \sqrt{s(s - a)(s - b)(s - c)}$$

where $s = \dfrac{a + b + c}{2}$

Fig. 7.—In this diagram:

$a : b :: b : c$ or $\dfrac{b^2}{a} = c.$

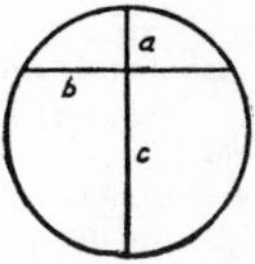

FIG. 7

179

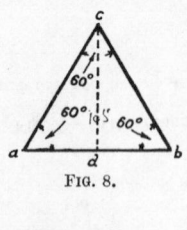

FIG. 8.

Fig. 8.—In an equilateral triangle $ab = 1$, then $cd = \sqrt{0.75} = 0.866$, and $ad = 0.5$; $ab = 2$, then $cd = \sqrt{3.0} = 1.732$, and $ad = 1$; $cd = 1$, then $ac = 1.155$ and $ad = 0.577$; $cd = 0.5$, then $ac = 0.577$ and $ad = 0.288$.

Fig. 9.—In a right-angled triangle with two equal acute angles, $bc = ac$. $bc = 1$, then $ab = \sqrt{2} = 1.414$; $ab = 1$, then $bc = \sqrt{0.5} = 0.707$.

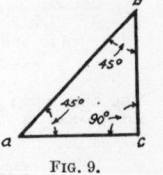

FIG. 9.

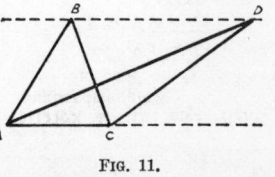

FIG. 10.

Fig. 10 shows that parallelograms on the same base and between the same parallels are equal; thus $ABCD = ADEF$.

Fig. 11 demonstrates that triangles on the same base and between the same parallels are equal in area; thus $ABC = ADC$.

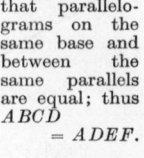

FIG. 11.

180

INDEX

A

B

187

191